THE NAKED-EYE SKY

(No Telescope Needed)

Second Edition

James R. Sowell

Sowell & Sons Publishing

Atlanta, GA

For information about permission to reproduce selections from this book, write to

Permissions

Sowell & Sons Publishing

2472 Sunset Drive

Atlanta, GA 30345

ISBN: 978-0-615-33181-2

Library of Congress Control Number: 2009911227

Printed and bound in the United States of America

McQuiddy Classic Printing

Nashville, TN

2011

To my Shining Stars
Virginia,
Daniel and Thomas,
and my parents
Bob and Anne

Foreword

I have written this guide for the budding astronomy enthusiast who wants to learn about the night sky. You are not ready to buy a telescope or join an astronomy club, and you have some basic questions but don't want to be overwhelmed by math and physics. You are ready to take the first step, but how do you begin? This is the guide for you. Think of me as your next-door neighbor, backyard astronomer, and together we are watching the sun set and the stars come out on a crisp October evening.

The Naked-Eye Sky describes astronomical objects and explains daily, monthly, and yearly phenomena. We will learn why the Earth has seasons and the Moon goes through phases. I'll introduce you to the constellations, a few stars, and even a galaxy – all of which you can see without a telescope or pair of binoculars. In fact, there are no pictures in this book taken with a telescope – we only need our eyes to see the sights. If you want a giant coffee-table book of the latest Hubble Space Telescope photographs – and I own some of those books – then this one is not for you. Rather, this guide should go with you on campouts.

The intent is to begin slowly with each topic at a very basic level. Numerous diagrams are provided to help you visualize the concepts. At the end there is a glossary and several tables of information. No matter how many aids are provided, though, you will need to go outside and make naked-eye observations yourself – whether it is the changing phases of the Moon, the lengthening of daylight in the Spring, the view of Venus as an Evening Star, or the annual occurrence of a meteor shower. It is just like a swimming course – you can read about it to understand the concepts, but you have to jump in and do it. With astronomy, there is no chance of sinking, and I hope you never get tired of the view.

Contents

INTRODUCTION

Astronomy can provide a great many joys and wonders through a variety of ways. People have often thought that they must have a telescope to see anything of interest, but this is far from the case. Besides the Sun, Moon, and Earth, which are all easily visible astronomical objects, the average human eye can see thousands of stars, five planets, numerous clusters, a handful of gas or dust clouds, and even a galaxy or two. We will learn about all of them.

It is true that a telescope is needed to see a host of items. These include many distant or intrinsically faint objects, such as quasars and black holes, respectively, and they are not covered here. Furthermore, some topics, such as the Big Bang theory and the description of the Universe, are beyond the intent of this guide.

The main topics are (1) the workings of the Sun, Moon, and Earth, (2) the recognition and mythology of the major constellations, and (3) the identification and explanation of numerous heavenly bodies and associated phenomena that are visible without the aid of a telescope. To begin, let's have a quick overview of the main players.

Our local region of space is ruled by the Sun. It contains most of the material (mass) of the Solar System, and consequently dominates the mechanics of the orbiting bodies because of its strong gravity. It also provides the constant light that has been sustaining life on our planet for billions of years. There are eight planets[1] circling around the Sun: Mercury, Venus, Earth, Mars, Jupiter, Saturn, Uranus and Neptune. A mnemonic to remember their order is "My Very Energetic Mother Just Served Us Nothing." Not all of the planets have moons; to date there are more than 100 known moons.

The planets and moons are composed – to varying degrees – of rock, ice, and gas. The distinction between these and stars is that stars create energy by thermonuclear reactions in their deep cores. Why an object is either a star or a planet is purely dependent upon the total amount of mass (material or stuff) it has. Planets do not have enough mass to begin the nuclear reactions in their interiors.

We will also examine eclipses, comets (dirty snowballs), meteors (rocky chunks a few yards in size), star clusters, galaxies, and several other celestial objects and phenomena.

---

[1]Although Pluto is now classified as a "Dwarf Planet", I will sometimes include it in the text as a planet.

SIZES AND DISTANCES

Measurement Units

Many people find the Heavens to be incomprehensible because of the great range in sizes and distances. Even astronomers have a difficult time coming to grips with quantities like the distance from the Earth to the Sun when it is expressed as $93,000,000$ miles ($150,000,000$ km). The way to comprehend sizes and distances is to use meaningful measurement units.

Here is an example. The distance from my house in Atlanta to my parents' house north of Nashville is about 280 miles. The number 280 is just on the verge of our ability to comprehend its magnitude. I could state that the distance is $17,740,000$ inches – the number is correct but it is completely meaningless because we do not have a real-world feel for numbers that large. An even better way of relating the distance between the houses is to say it takes me four hours to drive from one to the other. In expressing it that way, two things have happened: (1) the quantity of four hours is small and easily comprehensible and (2) the measurement units were switched from distance to time. Hopefully by this change in units, you get a better feel for the distance between these two homes.

A long time ago, astronomers recognized the need for better distance measurement units in the Solar System, Galaxy, and Universe, since the mile is just too short. The standard unit for the Solar System is based on the average distance from the Earth to the Sun. Instead of using 93 million miles (150 million km), this distance is defined as 1, and we call it the **Astronomical Unit** or 1 AU. With this relative scale, we find that the distance from the Sun to Mercury is 0.4 AU, to Mars it is 1.6 AU, to Jupiter 5.2 AU, and to Pluto it is on average about 40 AU.

The Astronomical Unit works great for the Solar System, but when we go to stellar distances it is too small. The nearest star is more than $300,000$ AU away, so again we have numbers that are too large for comprehension. Once more, we will use unit substitution, but this time we use the speed of light to describe the distances between stars. Light travels at about 186,000 miles per second ($300,000$ km per second). So in one second, light has traveled $186,000$ miles; in two seconds it has gone $372,000$ miles. Let the clock run for one entire year, and the light will have traveled 5.9×10^{12} miles (9.5×10^{12} km) or $63,240$ AU. The distance that light travels in one year is defined as 1 **Light Year**. The nearest star is about four light years away (distance), or you can say that the light emitted by this star takes four years (time) to travel the expanse of space between us.

Light travel time can also be used in the Solar System, but a year is much too long. It takes light about a second to go from the Moon to the Earth, and it takes sunlight just eight minutes to reach us. We see Jupiter the way it was 30 to 40 minutes ago. The reflected light off tiny Pluto takes about five hours to reach us. This delay becomes noticeable when we are communicating with astronauts or spacecraft.

Scale Size of the Solar System

To further visualize the size of the nearby astronomical bodies, let's do a mental exercise. I am going to shrink the Sun down from its diameter of 865,000 miles (1,392,000 km) to 12 inches, which is the size of a basketball or typical beach ball. Likewise, the diameters of and distances to the planets have been correspondingly shrunk. The diameter of the Earth would be about the size of a BB. Jupiter, the largest planet, would be slightly smaller than a ping-pong ball, and Saturn is the size of a quarter coin. As we will see, though, the range in size is much less dramatic than the change in distances.

To grasp the distances, I place the beach ball on the 50-yard line in the center of a football field (see the two nearby diagrams, which are drawn to scale). Mercury is only 15 yards away, Venus is 25 yards away (hence its orbit touches the sideline), and the Earth is 35 yards away, so it reaches the players' benches. Mars' orbital radius of 55 yards puts it up in the spectators' bleachers. Then there is a big jump in the spacing between the outer planets. Jupiter is 190 yards away, and Saturn's distance of 340 yards places it out beyond the parking lots. Uranus and Neptune are 690 and 1080 yards distant, respectively. Lastly, Pluto, with its highly eccentric orbit, at 1420 yards is almost 0.8 miles away, a very far cry from that of Mercury just 15 yards from the beach ball.

On this scale, how far away is the next nearest beach ball (star)? Would it be five miles? ten miles? twenty miles? Actually, it is much farther – 2000 miles away! The spacing between stars is immense!

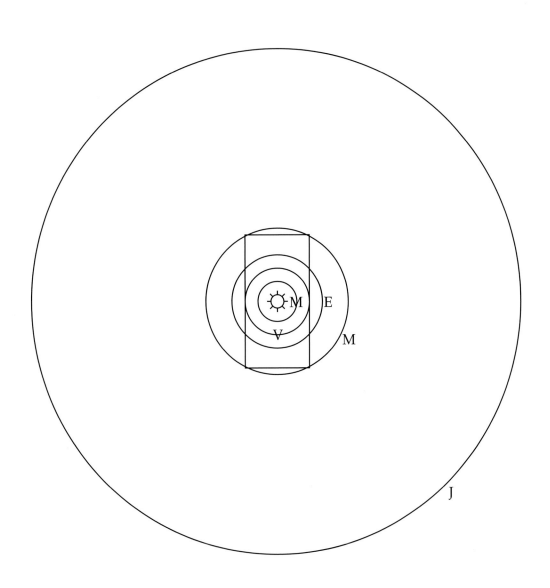

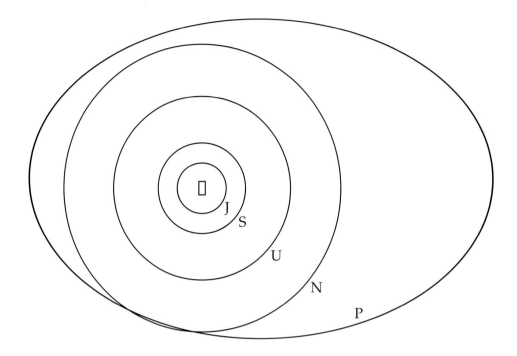

A quick comment must be made about masses because pounds, kilograms, and tons are much too small. For Solar System objects, masses relative to the Earth are used. Two cases would be Venus at 0.81 Earth masses and Jupiter having 317.8 Earth masses. Stellar masses are always expressed in terms of the Sun's mass, which is about 300,000 Earth masses.

The following table is a summary of distances, sizes, and masses for the eight planets and Pluto. It includes actual values along with those based on shrinking the Sun to 12 inches. The diagram shows the relative sizes of the planets.

Planet	Distance		Diameter		Mass
	(AU)	(yd)	(E=1)	(in)	(E=1)
Mercury	0.39	15	0.38	0.04	0.06
Venus	0.72	25	0.95	0.10	0.81
Earth	1.00	35	1.00	0.10	1.00
Mars	1.52	55	0.53	0.05	0.11
Jupiter	5.20	190	11.20	1.13	317.80
Saturn	9.54	340	9.41	0.95	94.30
Uranus	19.18	690	4.11	0.42	14.60
Neptune	30.06	1080	3.81	0.39	17.20
Pluto	39.44	1420	0.17	0.02	0.01

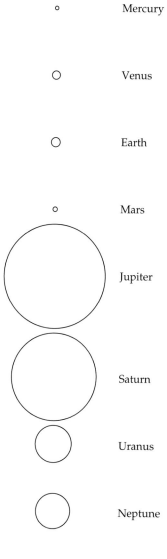

Mercury

Venus

Earth

Mars

Jupiter

Saturn

Uranus

Neptune

THE SUN AND MOON

THE SUN

Movement in the Sky

Although astronomy is most often associated with the night sky, we will begin our study with the Sun. The Sun and Earth are the two most important objects in the Universe for our existence. The Sun in many ways is the ruler of our daily lives. There is a constant "cosmic dance" between the Sun and Earth, and we need to understand the motions involved. We will see what is physically occurring and how it observationally appears to us.

There are two motions at work. Let's look at each one individually. First, there is **rotation** – the *spinning* of the Earth on its axis. The rotation of the Earth gives us night and day. Although the Sun appears to be the one in motion across the sky, it is actually the rotation of the Earth that causes the Sun, Moon, and stars to rise in the East, move across the sky, set in the West, and reappear the next day in the East.

The second motion is that of the Earth's orbit around the Sun. Motion around another object due to gravity is called **revolution**. [Note that we do not always use the terminology properly. For example, the motion of a car engine is called RPMs – revolutions per minute – but actually the crankshaft is rotating.] The Earth's revolution around the Sun gives us our year. A year is much longer than a day so the changes that are associated with the Earth's revolution, such as the seasons, take longer to occur than the changes from rotation (day to night and back).

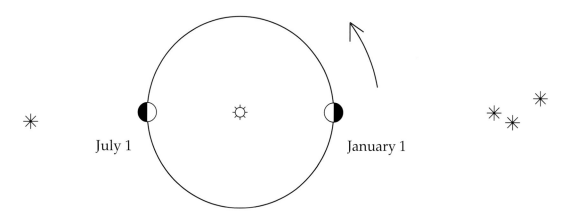

July 1   January 1

Both of these motions have an effect on the heavenly bodies. As I've already pointed out, the daily, or *diurnal*, rotation of the Earth gives us night and day, and this moves the Sun and stars across the sky. Let's put both motions together now and pick a date, say January 1. At midnight we are viewing stars that are in the opposite direction from that of the Sun (we are looking straight overhead). At noon, while looking straight overhead, we see the Sun. Now those stars we saw 12 hours ago are directly behind us. (You might want to refer to the diagram above.) Let's jump ahead to July 1. What has happened? The Earth has revolved halfway around in its orbit. At noon, the Sun is still straight overhead, but we are now looking in the direction of those stars we saw back on January 1 at midnight. The stars we see this midnight are in the opposite direction. We did not see these stars six months ago because they were behind the Sun. During this half-orbit our seasons have changed and so have the visible stars.

Positions in the Sky

Before we begin in earnest to examine the motions of the Sun and other celestial objects, we need to define a few coordinate terms. Astronomers often use a coordinate system on the sky similar to that used on the Earth. Latitude and longitude lines are projected up on the Celestial Sphere as if there were a light at the center of the Earth. On the sky are projections of the Equator and the North and South Poles. To distinguish these from the terrestrial ones, they are called the **Celestial Equator** and **Celestial Poles**. Your **zenith** is the point straight over your head. Your **meridian** is a line of longitude that passes through the Celestial Poles and your zenith. The meridian cuts your sky in half. Two people in different locations will have different meridians and zeniths, but the Celestial Equator and Celestial Poles are the same for all.

Although the Earth is in orbit around the Sun, to us it looks as if the Sun is the moving body. Again, there are two motions – the rotation and the revolution of the Earth. If the Earth did not rotate, we could easily see the apparent motion of the Sun in front of the background stars as the Earth orbited it. This path on the sky is called the **Ecliptic**. The axis of the Earth's rotation is tilted 23.5° to the Ecliptic, so the Sun spends half a year North of the Celestial Equator and the other half South of it. It is because of this tilt that the Earth has seasons. Let's see why.

Use your imagination and hover thousands of miles to the side of the Earth. From your vantage point, the Sun is to your left, so as you look on the Earth, the left half is in sunlight, while the right half is experiencing night. Where is the North Pole – is it in the day or night half? Will it change during the course of a year? We would constantly see that half of the Earth is in light, the other half not. And, we would see the North Pole move from an extreme position in the day side toward an extreme position in the night side and back during the year. The extreme position in the day side occurs on June 21 and the extreme night side position is around December 21. During the journey of the North Pole position, twice during the year it lies on the day-night boundary. These dates are usually March 20 and September 23.

Summer   Winter

Our view is that the Sun changes position in the sky with respect to the background stars. During Summer, the Sun is high on the sky; during Winter it is low. Let's move from my Atlanta location down to the Equator. On March 20 and September 23, the Sun will be straight over our heads at noon. On June 21, the Sun would be as far North as we would see it move, and likewise on December 21, it would be as far South as it ever got. So if every day at noon, we recorded the position of the Sun from December 21 to June 21 we would see it move from 23.5° South of the equator to 23.5° North of it. From June 21 to December 21, the motion would be from the North to the South. On the dates of June 21 and December 21, the Sun changes its direction of motion.

These two dates are known as the **Summer** and **Winter Solstices** – "Sun Stands Still." The two dates in the middle, March 20 and September 23, are times when the Sun is directly over the Equator at noon. These dates are the **Vernal** and **Autumnal Equinoxes** – dates of "Equal Night" and day. [Please note that on the Summer Solstice, the day is not longer – it is still 24 hours long. However, the amount of *daylight* during this 24-hour period is a maximum.]

You do not have to be at the Equator to see the position of the Sun change during the year. You can move North or South of it and you will still see this motion. When you get to 23.5° North of the Equator, on June 21 the Sun will be at your zenith. [Your zenith is the point directly over your head.] This latitude is called the Tropic of Cancer. For an observer at any latitude North of the Tropic of Cancer, you would still see the motion of the Sun throughout the year, but the Sun would never reach your zenith. The corresponding latitude at 23.5° South of the Equator is the Tropic of Capricornus. The Sun is in the constellation of Cancer on June 21 and in Capricornus on December 21.

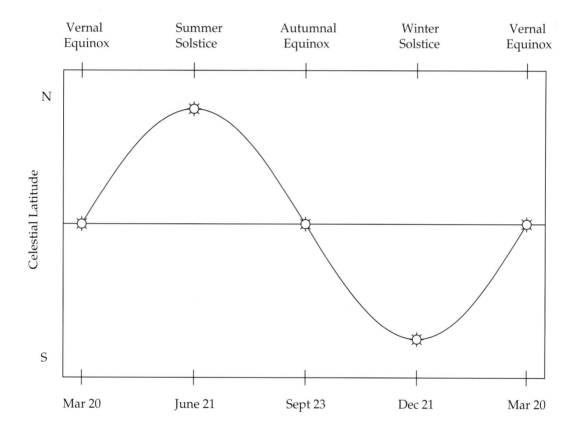

Seasons

Contrary to popular belief, the seasons are not a result of a change of distance from the Sun. It is true the Earth's orbit is not an exact circle, so there is a date (around January 4) when we are actually the closest to the Sun, but the change in distance has little to no effect on producing the seasons. It is unfortunate that many astronomy textbooks have portrayed the Earth's orbit with an exaggerated ellipse, for this misperception has been hard to dispel.

To explain the seasons, let's first review exactly what occurs meteorologically during the course of a year. There is a season of high temperature, one of low temperature, and two moderate seasons in between. There are different weather patterns, too. For now, let's focus on the amount of heat.

Given a source, such as a bright table lamp, there are different ways to heat an object, like a flat desktop. The first way is to change the distance from the lamp to the desktop, but, as already explained, this is not the cause for the seasons. A second way is to put in a brighter light bulb. This too does not explain the seasons, for the Sun has fortunately maintained a very constant luminosity for billions of years. A third approach deals with the angle that the light shines down.

We are going to keep shining the lamp on the same spot on the desktop. We are not going to change the distance from the spot, but we are going to move the lamp to different angles so that it is not just straight overhead. Think how sunrise begins on the horizon, travels up to higher angles, reaches high noon, and then begins traveling down to sunset on the opposite horizon. Likewise, we can angle the lamp to shine directly toward the desktop's edge, then increase its angle above the desktop, and eventually place it straight overhead. We can even shine from beneath, and this would correspond to night since no light would illuminate the desktop.

Now put the table lamp at high noon. Furthermore, let's take a hollow pipe and suspend it below the lamp. The inner area of the pipe is exactly equal to the round spot of light on the desktop. Turn the lamp on for one second and for the sake of argument, let's say that one million photons traveled through the pipe and hit the circular patch on the desktop. Now move the lamp and pipe to a 45° angle, which would approximate the Sun at either 9 am or 3 pm. Again we turn on the lamp for one second and another one million photons travel through the pipe. Although the diameter has not changed, we observe that the amount of illuminated area on the desktop is larger and fainter.

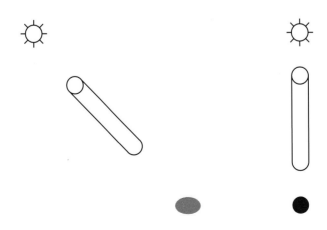

During one second, the number of photons that travel through the pipe does not change, but the size of the lighted, heated area does vary. When the lamp is straight overhead, the light is concentrated into the smallest area. At this position, the heating is most *effective* because the number of photons per area is highest. This is witnessed every day. In theory the hottest time of the day would be noon, for the Sun is straight overhead, or at least as high in the sky as it will get. It turns out that our days are hottest a couple of hours later, but that is due to the retention of heat by the land, air, and water.

Let's now return to the seasons. During the year, the Sun's track across the sky moves northward and then southward. For the regions on the Earth near the equator, the Sun is always close to the zenith and there is little difference between the seasons, which are always hot. Likewise, the Arctic and Antarctic lands are continuously frigid because the Sun stays near the horizon and the sunlight strikes the ground at a low angle. For those of us in the mid-northern latitudes, the Sun is the highest in the sky during June, July, and August. Consequently, the effective heating is the greatest then and we experience Summer. During these same three months, the mid-southerly latitudes see the Sun at its lowest position. The effective heating is therefore rather weak, so they are experiencing Winter. Six months later the situation is reversed for these two hemispheres. The two milder seasons of Spring and Fall are in between. The large changes in seasonal temperatures are due to the wide variation in the Sun's angle above the ground. This is why the Earth's mid-latitude areas are called the Temperate Zones.

To summarize the reasons for the seasons:

(1) The Earth's rotation axis is tilted by 23.5° with respect to its orbit;

(2) This tilt causes the height (altitude) of the Sun to vary cyclically throughout the year as the Earth revolves; and

(3) The amount of heat per ground area is greatest when the Sun is high in the sky, nearest to the zenith, and lowest when the Sun's altitude is low.

THE MOON

We now begin our study of the night sky and start with the Moon. I am sure you have observed the Moon on numerous occasions. You have probably already seen many of the phenomena that are described below. After understanding the explanations, please continue to watch the Moon. You are witnessing the mechanics of the Universe in motion!

Phases

We mentioned before that the Earth has two motions: revolution around the Sun and rotation around its axis. We now add a third motion – that of the Moon's orbit (revolution) around the Earth. First, though, we will pause the revolution and rotation of the Earth and look at only the Moon's revolution. To get a better observational perspective, let's move to our position above the Solar System. We have the Sun to the right and the Earth in the center. From this vantage point, the Moon's orbital motion is in a counterclockwise direction around the Earth.

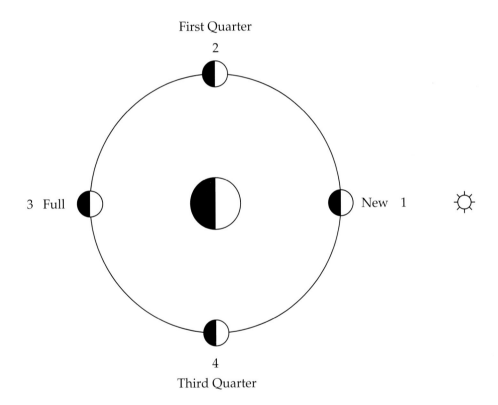

Our view of the Earth is straight down onto the North Pole, and we see half of the Earth in daylight, the other half in darkness. The Moon is drawn at four locations in its orbit. Note the Moon's shadow pattern. Half of the Moon is always illuminated by the Sun, whereas the other half is not. Let's look at position 1 of the Moon's orbit (New). Notice that all three bodies are in line: the Sun, Moon, and Earth. In order to see the Moon, a viewer must be in daylight. Furthermore, the Moon is in the direction of the Sun. Imagine for a second that a lamp is the Sun, you are the Earth, and a baseball is the Moon. Held at arm's length, the ball is difficult to see because of the lamp's bright glare, and the same is true of the Moon when it is near the Sun in the sky. In addition, you are looking at the unlit, dark side of the Moon. This phase is **New Moon**.

Now we skip to position 3 (Full). Although the Sun, Moon, and Earth are again in line, the Earth and Moon have switched positions. An observer on the night side of the Earth sees the illuminated side of the Moon. Let's think again about viewing a baseball held at arm's length, but now the bright lamp is behind you. In this orientation you see all of the sunlit side of the baseball. This is **Full Moon**.

Positions 2 and 4 are times when half of the Moon's bright disk is visible to the Earth. These are the **First** and **Third Quarter Moons**. The nomenclature is poor. At any one time, half of the Moon is always illuminated by the Sun. During the Quarter Moons, "half" of the disk is seen. The expression of Quarter Moon has to do with its position in its orbit. New Moon is considered the start of the lunar cycle. First Quarter Moon is one-fourth of the orbital period, Full Moon is half, and Third Quarter Moon is three-fourths.

This is a good time to stress a key point – the phase of the Moon has no correlation with the time of day, or for that matter, day of the week or time in the year. It is purely a function of the positions of the Sun, Earth, and Moon. As the Moon revolves, the amount of the illuminated side that is visible to the Earth changes. The phase of the Moon is not due to the Earth's shadow obscuring part of the lunar disk.

At the start of this section, we stopped the Earth's revolution and rotation, but now let us allow the Earth to spin again. Although we are standing on a spherical planet, due to its large size our visible world appears flat, the edge of which is the horizon. For our idealized observer, he/she will see the Sun rise in the East, be straight overhead on your meridian six hours later at noon, and set in the West six[2] hours later still. In the following diagram, at position 1 the observer is oriented so the Sun is directly above – this is noon. At position 3 the Sun is directly below the ground, which is midnight. Obviously, at positions 2 and 4, the time is six o'clock, but which is dawn (sunrise) and which is dusk (sunset)? [Hint: From this vantage point above the plane of the Solar System, all of the planets orbit counterclockwise.] The Earth's rotation is in the same direction as its revolution, so the observer goes from position 1 (noon) to position 2 (sunset). Therefore, position 4 is sunrise.

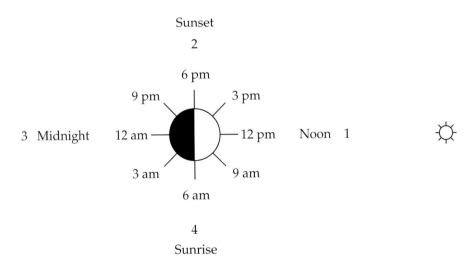

[2]For a variety of reasons, including the change in seasons, the times of rising and setting of the Sun and Moon vary somewhat.

The next diagram is a combination of the previous two. Let's first think about when the Moon is overhead *at particular times of the day*. We'll start with New Moon. This phase is the easiest to understand because the Moon is in exactly the same direction as the Sun. The Sun and New Moon are directly overhead at noon. The Sun and New Moon rise at sunrise and set at sunset. At Full Moon the situation is exactly opposite. The Full Moon rises at sunset, is directly overhead at midnight, and sets at sunrise.

Look at the First Quarter Moon at position 2. Here the Moon is on the meridian at sunset. When did the First Quarter Moon rise? We know it is overhead at sunset and that it rose six hours previous. Backup six hours from sunset – that would be noon. Therefore, the First Quarter Moon rises at noon. To confirm that deduction, look at the Earth's noon position. At this time, the Sun is straight overhead and the First Quarter Moon is on the horizon 90° away.

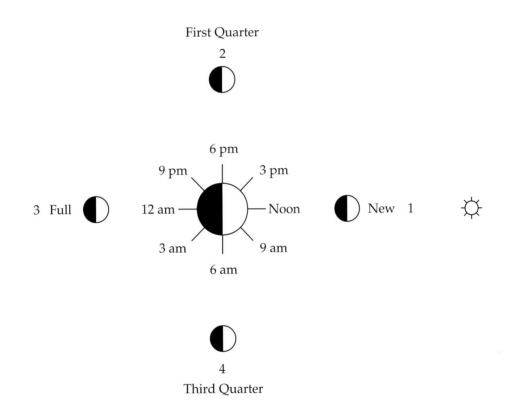

In summary,

1. The phase of the Moon is due entirely to the orientation of the Sun, Earth, and Moon.

2. The Moon rises in the East, (approximately) six hours later it is on the meridian, and six hours later still it sets in the West.

3. Although the phase of the Moon is not a function of the time of day, *for a given phase* the location of the Moon on the sky is dependent on the time. For example, the Full Moon always rises at sunset (sorry all you mystery writers, but you cannot change it.)

Before we continue, it is time for you to do an important observing exercise. It is best to start this a couple of days after New Moon, so check a calendar. Pick a consistent time of the evening to view the Moon, say 7 pm. Now, for a week or two, notice the following three changes: (1) the phase of the Moon, (2) its position on the sky, and (3) the brightness change. Realize that you are literally seeing the Moon orbit the Earth!

A simulation of the Moon in various phases.
(Photograph is by Midhat Becar.)

The Large, Red Moon on the Horizon

Many of you have no doubt seen the orange-red Moon rise shortly after sunset. Why is it orange-red and why is it so large? The first question is easy to answer. Go back to imagining a flat world. Above the flat land is a flat atmosphere. If you look straight overhead, the view through the atmosphere is the shortest. But as you look away from the zenith toward the horizon, the line of sight gets increasingly longer through the atmosphere. Different colors of light do not travel equally well through the thicker airmass. Blue light does not penetrate as well or as far as does red light. When the Moon and Sun are near the horizon, only the red and orange colors are able to pass through the thick atmosphere to us. [For more information, refer to the *Atmospheric Phenomena* section.]

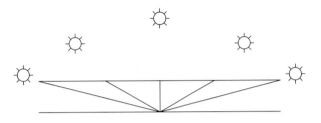

Sunset as seen from Dog Island, FL, on June 6, 2009.
(Photograph was taken by the author.)

The answer to the second question – why does the Moon appear so large near the horizon – is not nearly as clear cut. Scientists agree it is an optical illusion, but there is disagreement as to why. I have read theories that when we see the Moon near familiar objects, such as trees and buildings, we are better able to judge its size. I have also read that the eye and brain perform differently when looking directly up rather than horizontally. My own hypothesis is this: When the Full Moon is low on the horizon, it is not much brighter than the background sky because it is near the time of sunset; therefore, our pupils do not have to constrict much. When the Moon is overhead, it is much brighter than the background for twilight has ended. Consequently, the eye's pupil has to constrict, and I believe that the different pupil sizes play a role in the optical illusion phenomenon. However, I have absolutely no biological or medical evidence of any sort to substantiate my hypothesis.

The Full Moon shortly before the start of the February 2008 lunar eclipse.
(Photograph was taken by the author.)

Rotation of the Moon

Does the Moon rotate (spin) on its axis? This answer needs some observational data. Make it a point to look at the Full Moon on several occasions. You should convince yourself the same side of the Moon is shown to you at each Full Moon. Once you have familiarized yourself with this face, you should notice that at all First Quarter Phases the Full Moon face is toward you, but it is only half illuminated. Likewise, for those who get up early enough to regularly observe the Third Quarter Moon, it too reveals the Full Moon face, but it is the other half of the disk that is seen.

Remember that the Moon is in orbit around the Earth. To help us out, let's place an exaggerated mountain on the Moon that points directly at the Earth when the Moon is Full (see the figure below). Our observations show that this mountain is also pointing directly at us at First and Third Quarter Moons. The New Moon would show this orientation, too. Does the Moon rotate on its axis? Yes. If an object were spinning on an axis, during one rotation, an observer on the object would see 360° on the sky. The mountain during the course of one orbit manages to point at all 360° on the sky. The Moon does indeed rotate. It turns out that the Moon's revolution and rotation rates are equal. This is referred to as a 1:1 spin-orbit coupling, or another expression is that the Moon is *tidally locked*. There are numerous examples of tidally-locked moons orbiting around their parent planet.

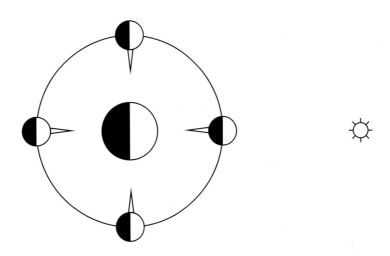

Darkside of the Moon

Is there a dark side of the Moon? Yes and no. The Moon has 50% of its surface illuminated at all times. Because the Moon rotates, the part of its surface in darkness changes. At Full Moon the mountain (in the previous diagram) is fully illuminated whereas at New Moon it is in darkness. There is no perpetually "dark" side of the Moon. A better expression is to refer to the "far" and "near" sides, for these do not change.

Earthshine

Have you ever seen a Crescent Moon and would swear you saw the outline of the rest of the Moon? Well, you have indeed seen it. This phenomenon is called **Earthshine**.

The Moon appears as a crescent because it is close to the New Moon phase, so we only see a little of the illuminated side. How is it that the "dark" side of the Moon is seen? Sunlight also impinges on the Earth, which happens to be a highly reflective world due to our clouds, ice caps, and oceans. Some of the reflected light hits the non-solar-illuminated side of the Moon, and a percentage of it in turn is reflected back to the Earth. The Earthshine is not nearly as bright as direct sunlight because of the extra reflections and the additional distance traversed. Earthshine is only visible for a few days during the Crescent Moon phases.

(Photograph was taken by Sorin Brinzei.)

ECLIPSES

Eclipses are special events one should never miss. There are two types: (1) **Lunar Eclipses** occur when the Moon moves into the Earth's shadow and (2) **Solar Eclipses** are caused by the Moon's shadow on the Earth.

Lunar Eclipse

In the section on the phases of the Moon, you should have begun to wonder why you are able to see a Full Moon. Shouldn't the Moon be in the Earth's shadow at this time? You have probably witnessed a few eclipses and numerous Full Moons, so by your own observations you infer that something else is involved, and that is indeed the case. The diagram below shows the orbit of the Moon around the Earth.

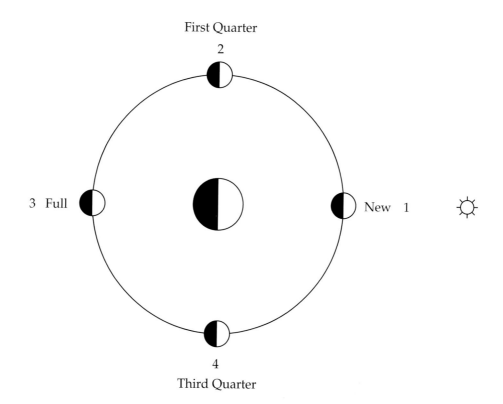

At Full Moon, the Moon is in line with the Earth and Sun – so why isn't the Moon in the Earth's shadow? The deception is because the figure is only showing two of the three dimensions of the Moon's orbit. The next diagram shows a side view – the orbit of the Moon around the Earth is tilted by 5° to the Ecliptic (the angle is exaggerated in the diagram). This value does not seem like much, but for comparison, how large is the angular size of the Full Moon on the sky? It is only half of a degree (0.5°). So the full extent of the change of the Moon's position above and below the Ecliptic is 20 times its own diameter!

25

The size of the Earth's shadow at the distance of the Moon's orbit is also a factor. It is $\sim 1.5°$ or about three times the size of the Moon's diameter. So, although the Moon can easily fit completely inside the Earth's shadow, it can be significantly above or below it at the time of Full Moon.

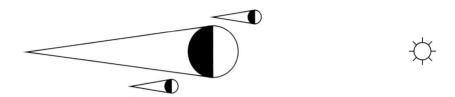

Now let's consider a **Lunar Eclipse**. Recall that the revolution of the Moon around the Earth is in the same direction as the motion of the Earth around the Sun, namely counterclockwise. The Moon is in orbit around the Earth, so it moves into the Earth's shadow. There are two types of lunar eclipses: partial and total. A **partial eclipse** occurs when the Moon's disk is not completely within the shadow of the Earth, whereas it is completely within during a **total eclipse**. The maximum duration for a total eclipse is 1 hour and 42 minutes. Because lunar eclipses occur during Full Moon, the middle of the eclipse event is always near midnight.

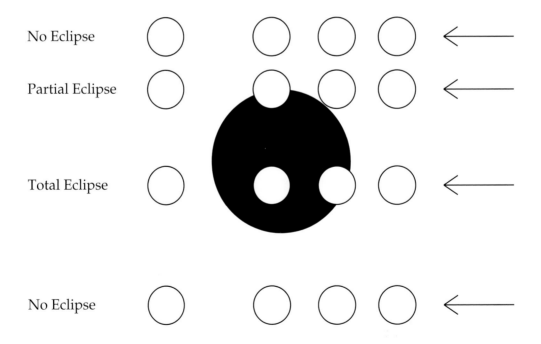

During a lunar eclipse, the shadow's curved edge is seen. The ancient Greek astronomers noticed that every eclipse has this characteristic. Being experts in geometry, they reasoned correctly that (1) the Moon was entering the Earth's shadow and (2) the Earth was spherical, for that is the only perfect geometrical solid that would always cast a curved edge. For example, a cube would not.

Today lunar eclipses provide little scientific returns other than a gross study of the Earth's atmosphere. Remember that when the Full Moon is on the horizon it has a red color since only these wavelengths pass through the thick atmosphere. During a lunar eclipse the reason we can see the faint Moon is because some sunlight passes through the Earth's atmosphere, hits the Moon, and reflects back to us. This light is highly reddened due to its long path through the Earth's atmosphere, so the eclipsed Moon usually has an orange-red tint. The extent of this tint, though, depends on your location. Different viewers sometimes see a different tint due to varying levels of atmospheric aberrations.

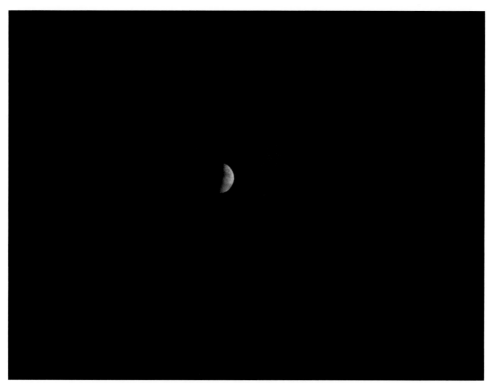

The Moon has entered the Earth's shadow (February 2008).
(Photograph was taken by the author.)

On some rare occasions, the tint may be slightly blue. This is also caused by the Earth's atmosphere, but the mechanism is completely different. Blue light is the most easily scattered or deflected light by small particles. Volcanoes put large amounts of dust into the upper atmosphere. This dust scatters the sunlight and produces beautiful sunsets and sunrises.

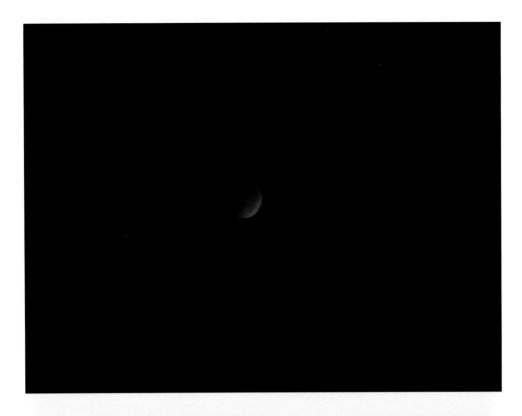

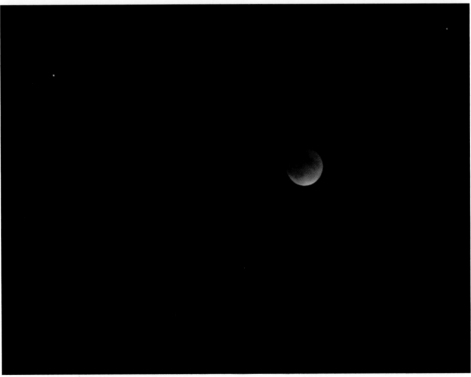

Totality during the Lunar Eclipse of February 2008. Notice the red color of the Moon compared to the previous two photographs. The bottom picture includes Saturn to the left and the star Regulus (in Leo) to the upper right.
(Both photographs were taken by the author.)

Solar Eclipses

A **Solar Eclipse** is the obscuration of the Sun by the Moon. At which lunar phase does a solar eclipse occur? New Moon – because the Moon must be in the same direction in the sky as the Sun. We are quite fortunate that the angular sizes of the Sun and Moon are both nearly equal. There is no science behind this, it just turns out the ratio of diameter-to-distance is about the same for both.

There are three varieties of solar eclipses: partial, total, and annular. The **total** and **partial eclipses** are directly analogous to the lunar cases, i.e., the Sun is either totally or partially blocked by the Moon. Because the orbits of the Earth and Moon are not exactly circular, the distances and angular sizes of the Sun and Moon vary. Although the change is not much, one can have the occurrence where the angular size of the Moon is less than that of the Sun. So, even if the centers of the two bodies are aligned, the Moon does not completely block out the Sun. This is an **annular eclipse**.

Since the Sun and Moon have almost exactly equal angular sizes, the length of a total eclipse must be rather short, and in fact the maximum duration is only 7.5 minutes. This also means the size and path of the shadow are rather small. So the number of people to have witnessed a total solar eclipse is much smaller than those who have seen a lunar eclipse. [The loss of the Sun was of great concern to ancient civilizations. The Chinese people banged on pots, pans, drums, etc., to scare away the dragon they believed was eating the Sun.]

(Photograph was taken by Alan Crawford.)

Compared to lunar eclipses, solar ones have provided much more science.

(1) As the Moon gradually blocks out the Sun, a very thin atmospheric layer is seen for a brief second. From the analysis of this layer's spectrum, the element helium (helios) was discovered prior to that on the Earth.

(2) At one time, the study of the corona, the beautiful halo of the Sun, was only possible during total eclipses. Now solar instruments, known as coronagraphs, can replicate an eclipse, so astronomers observe the corona at any time.

(3) Predictions from Albert Einstein's Theory of General Relativity about the bending of starlight by a gravitational body were confirmed in 1919 by comparing photographic positions of the stars with and without the eclipsed Sun in the pictures.

Viewing a Solar Eclipse

Special precaution must always be taken when viewing a solar eclipse. If precautions are not taken, then serious, permanent eye damage will occur. There are several very safe observing techniques:

(1) Put together a pinhole camera by making a tiny circular hole in a sheet of paper or metal. The hole's edge must be sharp – not ragged. The small hole acts as a camera lens. Allow the image to be projected several feet away.

(2) Reflect the solar image with a flat mirror onto a wall or sheet of paper.

(3) Use a safe, appropriate filter for direct viewing of the Sun.

(4) Use the leaves of trees as pinhole cameras. The view of hundreds of crescent Suns on the pavement or sidewalk will be one of the most memorable observations of your life.

Try to notice during the partial phases of the eclipse whether the overall brightness of the day seems to be changing.

TIDES

The tides are an effect primarily due to the pull of the Moon on the Earth and secondarily by the attraction of the Sun. The force of gravity between two objects is stronger when they are closer together than when farther apart. The Earth and Moon both have mass, so they both have gravity. The Earth has more mass, so it has a stronger attraction, which is why the Moon is in orbit about the Earth, rather than vice versa. [Actually, both bodies are in orbit around a center of mass, but this location is very near to the center of the Earth, and we do not notice the small motion of the Earth around it.]

The Moon does pull back on the Earth. Because the side of the Earth facing the Moon is nearer than is the far side, the force of gravity exerted by the Moon is stronger on the near side. This *differential* gravitational attraction slightly stretches the shape of the Earth from a sphere to an ellipse, as shown in the elongated diagram below.

Let's stop the orbital motions of the Earth and Moon, and now refer to the next diagram. The Earth is still going to rotate in a 24-hour period. With the starting location at the point nearest to the Moon, the surface has been pulled up away from a sphere (circle). Six hours later, you will rotate to a point where the surface is less than a sphere. Another six hours puts you back at a high point. During a 24-hour period, you will experience two high points and two low points.

Most of the surface of the Earth is water, and this fluidity causes the ocean tides. The Earth is stretched, but it is the movement of the oceans' water in response to this distortion that the tides occur. There will be two high and two low tides during a day. High tides occur when you are at the stretched locations on the Earth. Now, let us allow the Moon to revolve around the Earth. The stretched Earth will continue to point toward the Moon, but this orbital motion means successive

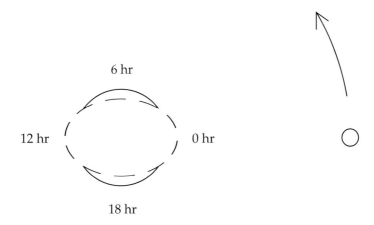

high tides are a little longer than 12 hours apart, since your favorite beach on the Earth has to catch up with the moving Moon.

Even if we did not have the Moon, we would still experience ocean tides because of the Sun's differential gravitation, but their magnitude would be significantly less. The effects of the Moon and Sun can be combined, too. When the Sun, Moon, and Earth are in line during New Moon and Full Moon, the combined gravitational stretching makes the highest high tides and lowest low tides. These are known as **Spring Tides**. Likewise, when the Moon is at First or Third Quarter Phases, the Moon is stretching the Earth in a direction perpendicular to that of the Sun's pull. The two effects do not cancel each other out, but the deviation from a sphere is the least, so the tides are not extreme. These are the **Neap Tides**.

Spring Tides

Neap Tides

ATMOSPHERIC PHENOMENA

As we gaze at the sky, we are looking through our atmosphere. The atmosphere contains a mixture of gases (primarily nitrogen and oxygen), water vapor, water drops, and water ice. The interaction of light from the Sun or Moon with the atmosphere can produce a variety of colorful phenomena.

Blue Sky

Why is our sky blue? Why not another color or multiple colors? The answer is actually quite simple. Most of the Earth's atmosphere consists of molecules of nitrogen (78%) and oxygen (21%), with trace amounts of argon and carbon dioxide. Sunlight consists of colors ranging from red to violet. [This is the *visible* light that we see. The Sun is also emitting infrared, ultraviolet, and even x-ray light.] The air molecules tend to deviate or scatter the Sun's light, but the effectiveness in scattering increases dramatically according to wavelength (i.e., color). For the shorter wavelengths of blue and violet light, the probability of being scattered is much higher than for the red light. So as the multi-colored sunlight hits the atmosphere, the blue light gets scattered all across the sky, creating the blue "glow."

Go outside and see that the blue color of the sky is not uniform. The darkest blue is straight overhead, and the shade of blue lightens toward the horizon. [Check this out on a perfectly clear day and again on a day with broken clouds. For the latter, notice that, for different altitudes above the horizon, the blue patches have very different shades, and many are a turquoise color.] The color is a function of the thickness of the atmosphere (refer to the section *The Large, Red Moon Near the Horizon*). The atmosphere is thinnest straight overhead, whereas near the horizon there are many more molecules for the Sun's light to pass through. There are so many molecules that other wavelengths of light get scattered, creating the different hues.

By the way, the Martian sky is pinkish-red. Its atmosphere is much thinner than ours, but contains a large amount of red dust picked up by winds from the Martian surface. Sunlight reflecting off this dust creates the pinkish-red sky.

Rainbows

Everyone has seen a rainbow created by water spraying from a hose. A rainbow in the sky is produced by exactly the same mechanism. Remember that white sunlight is a mixture of red, orange, yellow, green, blue, and purple light. [Sir Isaac Newton was the first to demonstrate this.] When white light passes through a clear, round water droplet, the droplet acts as a prism and is able to reflectively disperse the light into its constituent colors. Purple light is deviated the least, red the most. You can see this for yourself – note that the reds are always on the outer side of the rainbow, whereas the blues and purples are on the inside of the curve. To see a rainbow, you must have a low Sun behind you. So if the Sun is in the West, you will see the rainbow in the East. The best opportunity to see rainbows is immediately after an evening shower or storm.

(Photograph was taken by Stephen Cooke on November 15, 2008, in Blue Ridge, GA.)

Halos

In the cold upper atmosphere, water droplets freeze into ice. Cirrus clouds, unlike their cumulus cousins that are made of water vapor and droplets, are composed of ice. The ice crystals are tiny six-sided prisms, and these crystals refract the white sunlight into its many colors. **Refraction** (halos) and **Reflection** (rainbows) are opposites when it comes to orientation. To see the refractive phenomena from the ice crystals, you need to look in the general direction of the Sun or possibly the Moon. [For illustration, note that lenses refract light. To use a large magnifying lens, you would put the lens between the object and yourself, and you would look through the glass toward the object. But with a large mirror, a reflector, you would not only have to stand in front of it, but you would face toward the mirror and away from the object.]

The prism ice-crystals produce a colorful halo that can be a partial arc or can completely surround the Sun or Moon. The purple and blue light rays are deviated the least, so these colors are again on the inside of the arc. Because the ice crystals are six-sided, the various faces can each create halos or arcs. But since the angles between the faces are different with respect to the incident light, the resulting halos and arcs will appear at different angles (distances) on the sky. The most commonly seen halo is 22° away from the Sun, and the next most often is at 46°. The best opportunity for seeing halos and arcs is when the sky is covered with a calm, uniform layer of high cirrus clouds. The calmness is necessary to allow the ice crystals to "relax" and to arrange themselves into similar orientations.

I must again remind the reader to take special precaution whenever viewing objects near the Sun or the Sun itself. If cautions are not taken, then serious, permanent eye damage will occur. **Never look directly at the Sun with the naked-eye or though telescopes or binoculars, unless a suitable solar filter is employed.**

Sun Dogs

Sun Dogs, technically known as Parhelia, are a special aberration of light again created by the refraction of ice crystals. Unlike the halos, Sun Dogs are colorful "patches" that lie on either side of the Sun, parallel to the horizon. These patches can be several times the size of the Sun and can be very, very bright. The red side of the dispersed light is nearest to the Sun. Usually Sun Dogs are about 22° from the Sun, but because of their hexagonally-shaped ice crystals, Sun Dogs can be produced at much larger angles, but these are not common. [The name Sun Dog comes from these patches being close *companions* to the Sun.]

(Photograph was taken by the author.)

Green Flash

The Green Flash is a rare phenomenon seen at sunset. As the Sun sets on a very low horizon, preferably the ocean, the thick atmosphere of the Earth refracts the Sun's light by several degrees. As mentioned previously, the thick atmosphere creates the orange-red color of the setting Sun. The refracting atmosphere should allow a viewer to see the Sun set through the colors of the rainbow. The green flash is the instant that the dispersed green light is in your line of sight.

Northern Lights

The **Northern** and **Southern Lights** (the Aurora Borealis and Aurora Australis, respectively) are shimmering lights produced by high-speed particles emitted from the Sun that crash into upper-atmospheric air molecules. Besides light, the Sun gives off a rather steady stream of particles, primarily protons and electrons. This stream is called the Solar Wind. Both the proton and electron have electrical charges – the proton's is positive, the electron's is negative. When these particles reach the vicinity of the Earth, they encounter its magnetic field. One can imagine a magnetic field as a framework of lines emanating outward from the North Pole, extending above the equator, and then coming back down to the Earth near the South Pole. The magnetic field deviates charged particles from their previous direction, down along one of its field lines, toward either the North or South Pole. These particles hit the nitrogen and oxygen molecules high in the atmosphere. These collisions knock an electron out of its orbit into a higher orbit by giving it extra energy. Shortly afterwards, the electron gives up this extra energy in the form of a photon (light) as the electron returns to its initial orbit. The light emitted by this process is of a specific wavelength, which is directly coupled with the energy involved. The two most common colors seen are red and green.

Auroras are most brilliant when there are more particles coming from the Sun. The Sun has an approximately 11-year cycle in the number of spots on its surface and correspondingly on the number of solar wind particles. During the sunspot maximum, the large number of solar wind particles creates more auroras and compresses the ionosphere. Ham radio operators get significantly more "bounces" off the atmosphere and communicate over larger distances during these times.

Occasionally the Sun has a large, violent "explosion" on its surface. Such **solar flares** eject thousands of times more particles at much higher speeds than does the average solar wind. Spectacular solar flares are usually reported in the news media, for they can disrupt communications and electrical service. The light from a flare reaches the Earth about three days sooner than the charged particles. Viewers should be alert to the possibility of brilliant auroras, and those that usually do not get to see them (e.g., the southern US) should be prepared for a rare sighting.

Further Reading

Color and Light in Nature by D.K. Lynch & W. Livingston, (Cambridge University Press, Great Britain), 1995 [ISBN 0-521-43431-9]

Rainbows, Halos, and Glories by R. Greenler, (Cambridge University Press, Great Britain), 1980 & 1994 [ISBN 0-521-23605-3]

Light and Color in the Outdoors by M.G.J. Minnaert, translated and revised by L. Seymour, (Springer-Verlag, New York), 1993 [ISBN 0-387-07935-2]

TIMEKEEPING

Astronomers have always wanted to be able to predict future astronomical events, so timekeeping has been an important task.

There are three observational quantities: (1) the rotation of the Earth, (2) the revolution of the Moon around the Earth, and (3) the revolution of the Earth around the Sun. These define the day, month, and year, respectively. They are very independent mechanisms, and there is no reason why a "nice" or "exact" relationship should exist between them, like having precisely 365 days in a year.

The Day

We traditionally use the definition of the length of the day as the time from noon to the subsequent noon. At noon, the Sun is on the meridian, so this observation is relatively easy to make. But for our modern lives, there are serious problems with the application of this definition.

First, we have made the assumption that all motions of the Earth are uniform. This is not the case, for the Earth's orbit around the Sun is not an exact circle. The time it takes the Sun to move across the sky varies slightly in a regular pattern as the distance from the Sun changes. [The farther away we are from the Sun, the slower we move in our orbit, but the spinning of the Earth is constant.] To counter the variable solar rate across the sky, astronomers have defined the "mean solar day" as exactly 24 hours. The difference between the "apparent" and "mean" solar day can be as much as 17 minutes.

The second problem is that the Sun is not on your meridian at the same time it is on the meridian of a city 100 miles West of you. The American Railroads faced this dilemma in the mid-1800s, for each town had its own noon, based on the Sun being on their meridian. The solution was to define 24 global time zones. Within a wide zone, the time is standardized even though the Sun will probably not be on your meridian at noon. [This is why if you have a sundial, its time can be many minutes different from your watch's time. Also, do not forget about Daylight Savings Time, which puts it off by an hour.] Now, the use of the ficticious mean solar day allows us to all have watches with identical times, but the definition of the day is not being used exactly.

(Photograph was taken by David Elfstrom.)

The Month

If the Earth did not move around the Sun, then the Moon would take 27.32 days to go from one Full Moon to the next. With the Earth's orbital motion included, though, the total time between Full Moons is 29.53 days because the Moon has to travel longer to get the Sun, Earth, and Moon in line again. The additional day or two in most of our months is mankind's attempt to have exactly twelve months in one year.

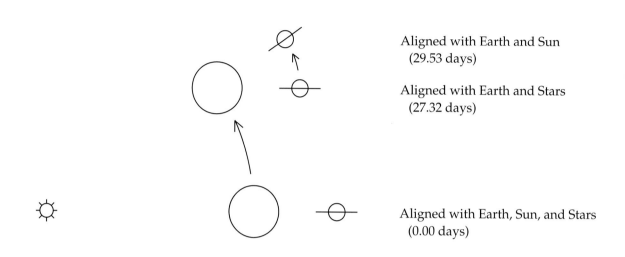

Aligned with Earth and Sun
(29.53 days)

Aligned with Earth and Stars
(27.32 days)

Aligned with Earth, Sun, and Stars
(0.00 days)

Speaking about the months, notice there is something peculiar about the names of the last four.

Month	Latin	English
September	Septem	Seven
October	Octo	Eight
November	Novem	Nine
December	Decem	Ten

September through December are the ninth through the twelfth months, not the seventh through the tenth. What happened? These months were shifted when Julius Caesar moved New Year's Day from March 1 to January 1 around 40 BC. [Later, the months July and August were named for Julius and Augustus Caesar, respectively.]

A final comment concerns a **Blue Moon**. This is the name for a second Full Moon in a calendar month. The only explanation I can give for the name is this second Full Moon is sad (blue or depressed) it did not get its own month.

The Year

Lastly, we see that the year is the time it takes the Earth to revolve once around the Sun. For the moment, let's think of the Earth as a spinning top. There is no reason why an integral number of spins should occur as the Earth orbits the Sun. [This is not always true of an orbiting body much less massive than the primary body, in which case the smaller object can have one face continually pointing toward the massive body. This is the case of the Moon and Earth.]

Due to inaccuracies in measurement, and probably the belief and desire that there should be a nice relationship between the year and day, Julius Caesar in 46 BC decreed that there are 365.2500 days in the year. The Julian Calendar, as this is known, began the practice of having a leap year (day) every fourth year.

The Julian Calendar is easy to understand and simple to use. Unfortunately, it is incorrect. There are actually 365.2422 days in a year, so the Julian Calendar is long (or slow) by 11 minutes and 14 seconds. That may not seem like a big deal, but by the time of AD 1582, this difference had compounded to ten days! The Catholic Church was getting concerned. The date for Easter is reckoned as the first Sunday after the first Full Moon after the Spring Equinox. But the Spring Equinox had shifted from March 21 to March 11, and the Church did not want Easter to move into the Winter Season. Pope Gregory XIII made two adjustments to the Calendar. The first was the removal of ten days. All Catholic countries went from October 4 to October 15, 1582. The effect of this was to put the date for the Earth's location in its orbit back to the situation at Caesar's time.

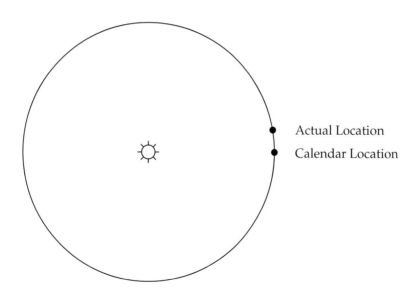

Actual Location

Calendar Location

The second correction was to the computation that determines the number of days in the year. The Julian Calendar criterion for the leap day was based on whether the year was evenly divisible by four. The Gregorian Calendar added two additional tests: First, if the year is evenly divisible by 100 (e.g., 1900), then it is NOT a leap year. Second, unless the year is evenly divisible by 400, then it would be a leap year. By this scheme, the years 2000 and 2400 are leap years but the years 1900, 2100, 2200, and 2300 are not. The improved accuracy of this computation will keep the calendar correct for more than 3000 years.

The switchover from the Julian Calendar to the Gregorian Calendar for the rest of the world occurred at various times. For Great Britain and the American colonies, the calendar jumped from September 2 to September 14, 1752. At this point, 11 days had to be dropped. Parliament enacted laws to prevent greedy landlords from collecting a full month's rent. This switchover is the basis for George Washington's birthday moving from February 11 on the "old" calendar to February 22 on the "new" one. By the way, Russia did not switch calendars until 1918, and they had to delete 13 days.

The Week

An interesting point to note is the week remained intact during these switchovers – the dates changed but, for example, Thursday still followed Wednesday. Why was the week held in such high esteem? And for that matter, why does the week have seven days, which occurred in almost all cultures – modern, primitive, and ancient?

The ancient civilizations saw seven "wanderers" in the sky: the Sun, Moon, and the five planets Mercury, Venus, Mars, Jupiter, and Saturn. A clue to the seven-day week is in their names. It is a little bit easier for the Spanish- and French-speaking cultures than for English speakers. In the table below, one sees that the Spanish day name is very similar to that of the object it commemorates. The English language has roots in northern European languages, and one sees the influence of Norse mythology, such as Woden's day is Wednesday and Thor's day is Thursday.

| ENGLISH | | | SPANISH | |
Day	Deity	Object	Day	Object
Sunday	Sun	Sun	Domingo	Sol
Monday	Moon	Moon	Lunes	Luna
Tuesday	Tiu (Tyr)	Mars	Martes	Marte
Wednesday	Woden	Mercury	Miercoles	Mercurio
Thursday	Thor	Jupiter	Jueves	Jupiter
Friday	Frigga	Venus	Viernes	Venus
Saturday	Saturn	Saturn	Sabado	Saturno

Other Cycles

Ancient and modern astronomers have kept track of other planetary cycles. When planets orbit the Sun, their year is a complete circuit with respect to the distant stars. But we watch the planets from a moving platform. What we see is a complete circuit from one alignment to the next one. An example would be the alignment of the Sun, Earth, and Mars. The next time this same alignment occurs, the orientation with respect to the stars will not be the same. This is the planet's **Synodic** period. The Mayans developed a synodic calendar that was useful for predicting the location of Venus.

Another type of tracking is to watch the planets travel along the Ecliptic. The Chinese calendar of twelve years is based on Jupiter's passage through twelve different constellations (e.g., the Rat, Dog, Monkey, etc.). The longest cyclic motion observed with the naked eye is the 30-year journey of Saturn along the Ecliptic.

CONSTELLATIONS

CONSTELLATIONS

Overview

The constellations are divided into five groups in the sky. There are the four seasonal groups, Winter, Spring, Summer, and Autumn. The fifth group, known as the Circumpolar Constellations, are visible year round. I have split this one into the Spring and Autumn groups. A section on the Zodiacal Constellations, which form a band around the sky, is also included.

The constellations are used to tell a story. For the ancients it may have been religious, or it may have been a map for traveling. Today we can still enjoy the stories associated with these stellar groupings. But it does take some imagination, not only with accepting the story, but also with "seeing" the person or object that the constellation represents. Constellations seem to fall into two categories – either they look exactly as described or they do not look like anything at all!

Constellations play another role today, too. These large areas on the sky can be used as a map to get you pointed in the right direction. We have all seen a US map that has each state shaded differently. We know that the states don't really appear that way, but for broad generalizations they work fine. For example, at a gathering of people one might say, "I am from Georgia". This description is fine for giving others a general idea of where you are from. For other purposes, though, you may have to be more specific – Telling the post office that you live in Georgia will probably not be enough information to get your mail delivered.

As we review the various seasons, I will describe how the constellations are a map on the sky. Usually we will start with a large, bright one, and we will find the other constellations from how they relate to each other. This is similar to starting at Georgia and going to Arizona one connecting state at a time. For example, the direct route would begin with Georgia, then Alabama, Mississippi, and so on. Two diagrams are provided for each season and constellation. The first consists only of stars, whereas the second has names added and outlines drawn to help you visualize the shape or description.

Winter Constellations

The Winter night sky has the brightest stars and some very impressive constellations. The most conspicuous is **Orion**. A circle of bright stars and constellations surround him, so it is very easy to identify them. In order around Orion are the bright stars Sirius (**Canis Major**), Procyon (**Canis Minor**), Pollux (**Gemini**), Castor (**Gemini**), Capella (**Auriga**), and Aldebaran (**Taurus**).

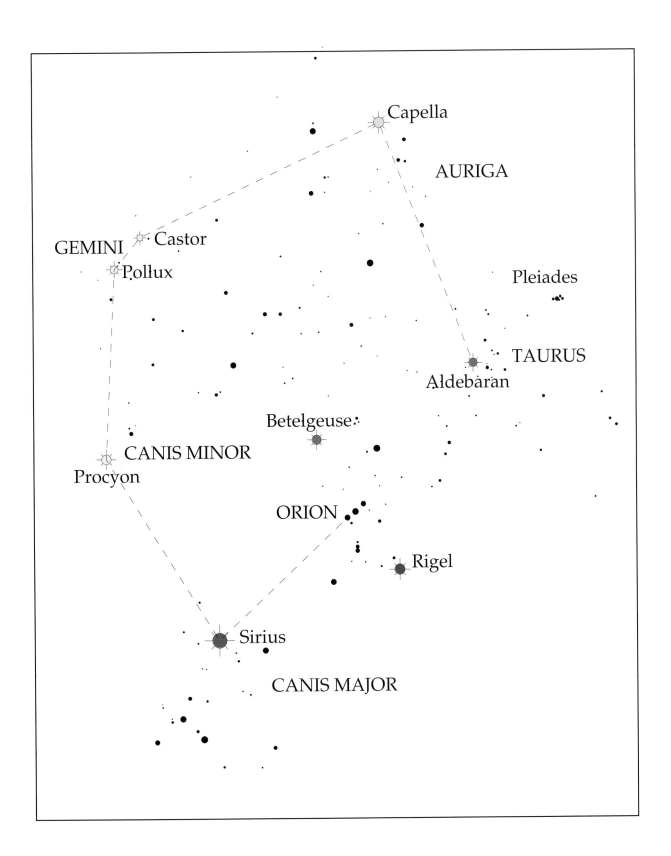

Capella

AURIGA

GEMINI

Castor

Pollux

Pleiades

TAURUS

Aldebaran

Betelgeuse

CANIS MINOR

Procyon

ORION

Rigel

Sirius

CANIS MAJOR

Orion

The Winter Constellations are dominated by the impressive Orion, the Mighty Hunter. This grand constellation looks exactly like a man. Many of its stars are very bright, and its distinguishing feature is its belt made of three stars. There are two bright stars below the belt that represent his knees; likewise, there are two shoulder stars. These can be seen even from bright urban areas. Hanging from his belt is a sword, and the middle "star" is a gaseous nebula known as the Great Orion Nebula (or M42)[3] [see the *Faint, Diffuse Objects* chapter for more information]. At a darker site, one will notice his right arm holds a club overhead, and in his left hand is a shield to protect him from the charging bull Taurus.

There are several different myths associated with Orion. One is he was a huge, mortal son of Neptune and was a great hunter. Another myth has it that Orion was killed by the sting of a scorpion sent by Gaia (Mother Earth) after he threatened to kill off all of the world's animals. For that reason, Scorpius and Orion are separated on the sky as far as possible, being Summer and Winter Constellations, respectively.

---

[3]The Messier Catalog is a list of 103 bright nebulous-like objects compiled by Charles Messier in 1781. This catalog includes gaseous nebulae, star clusters, and galaxies. Objects such as the Orion Nebula are referred to by the catalog's number, in this case M42.

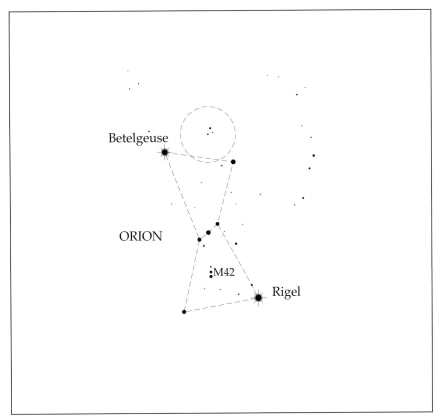

Canis Major

Being a hunter, Orion obviously had dogs with him. The first is Canis Major, the Big Dog. The three belt stars of Orion point directly toward the brightest star in the night sky, Sirius, which is known as the Dog Star. It is the eye (or head) of Canis Major. Sirius is one of the few stars in the night sky that is bright because it is nearby. Actually, most of the stars we see are extremely luminous, rare types of stars, and they are seen across great distances due to their prodigious luminosities. Besides the bright eye, the dog has a back, and three stars make out his hind legs, and a couple of others delineate forepaws. I tend to think of his appearance as that of a terrier. This constellation is close to the horizon, so it can often be partially obscured by trees.

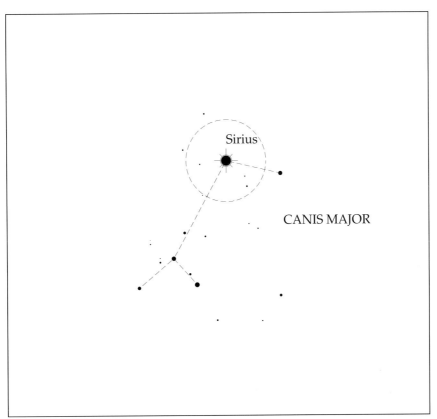

Sirius

CANIS MAJOR

Canis Minor

Whenever you see a constellation name with the word Major in it, then there must be a nearby one with Minor. These constellations tend to be smaller in size and to have fainter stars. To find Canis Minor, and all of the other Winter Constellations, we will follow a semi-circle around Orion. Begin with Sirius and make a clockwise arc around Orion (see the previous Winter Season diagrams). The first bright star you come to is Procyon, which is right in the middle of Canis Minor. It is pro- totypical of the second type of constellation – it bears absolutely no resemblance to its namesake, a dog. In fact, Procyon is about the only star that can be seen in the Little Dog. Several astronomers have therefore jokingly renamed him Spot! Actually, there is a second noticeable star, so you could say it is a hot dog.

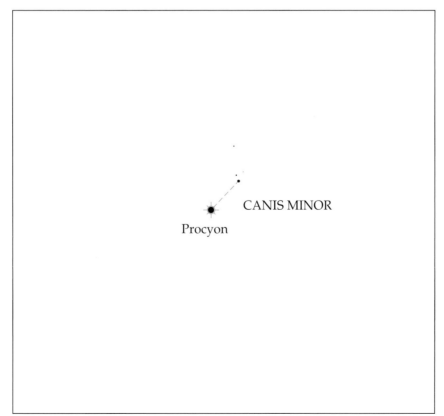

CANIS MINOR

Procyon

Gemini

Continuing on our arc around Orion, we get to two close stars that are about equally bright. These are the Gemini Twins, and they form the heads of the two brothers. These inseparable boys traveled with Jason and the Argonauts. The myth goes that Pollux was immortal but Castor was not. When Castor died, Pollux pleaded with Zeus to take away his own immortality so he could join his brother in Hades. Zeus felt it was inappropriate for Pollux to give up immortality, but as a compromise he gets to spend every other day in Hades with Castor.

There is an easy way to remember which of the twin stars is Pollux and which is Castor. Remember that we came up from Canis Minor, and its prime star is Procyon. The two "P" stars, Procyon and Pollux are nearest. As we continue our arc around Orion, the next bright star is Capella, so there are two "C" stars together, too.

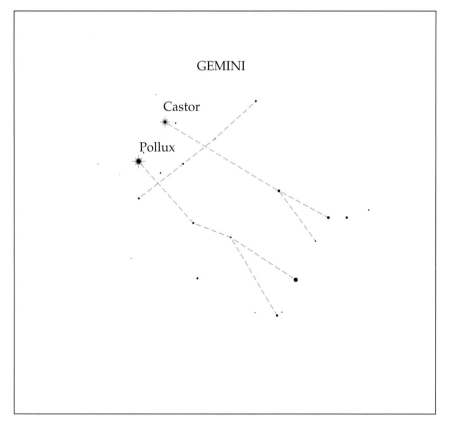

GEMINI

Castor

Pollux

Auriga

Auriga is a beautiful but somewhat schizophrenic constellation. The shape is either a pentagon or hexagon – it depends on how your eye cares to "connect" the stars. One of the myths regarding Auriga is he invented the Chariot. Some versions of the story state he was born crippled, others say that for some reason he made Zeus mad enough to throw him off of Mt. Olympus, which caused his lameness. In either case, Zeus was so impressed with the Chariot that he rewarded Auriga by placing him in the celestial sky. The other, completely different myth describes Auriga as a shepherd or goat herder. He is often drawn holding a small goat over his shoulders. There is a small cluster of stars near the hexagon known as "The Kids," and the Arabic translation of the bright star Capella is She-Goat. Indeed, two stories grafted together.

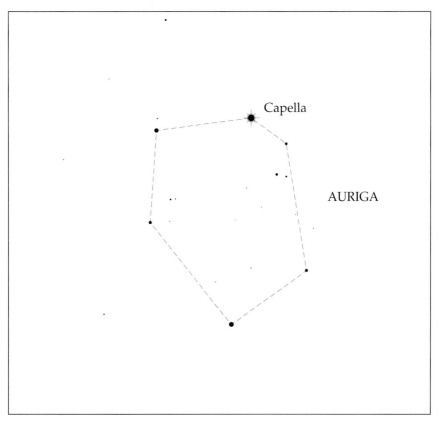

Capella

AURIGA

61

Taurus

The last of the Winter Constellations is Taurus the Bull. Continuing the arc from Capella we meet a red star named Aldebaran. It is at the top of a V-shaped set of five stars that form the bull's head. Aldebaran is described either as the red eye, tongue, or flames from the mouth. Taurus has two faint horns near the top of Orion's shield. He is charging up out of the ocean, so drawings typically depict only his front half.

Riding on the back of Taurus is the Pleiades star cluster. The Pleiades are not an independent constellation but are part of Taurus. Such a grouping is called an **asterism**. In the case of the Pleiades, they are a physical collection of about 200 stars known as an open cluster. The face of the bull, excluding Aldebaran, is another cluster called the Hyades. The Hyades are closer to us than the Pleiades so it appears larger and less concentrated.

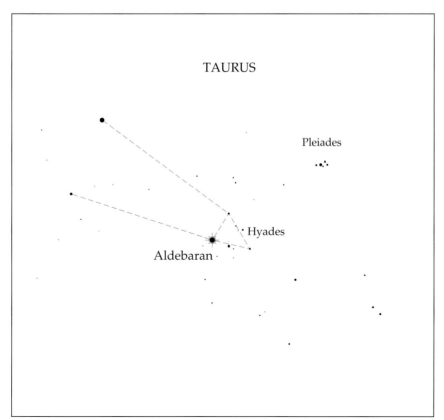

TAURUS

Pleiades

Hyades

Aldebaran

Spring Constellations

Ursa Major is the key Spring Constellation, and it will be used to find many other ones. Ursa Major, the Big Bear, contains the very familiar Big Dipper, another asterism. There is also a Little Bear, **Ursa Minor**. The myth regarding these two shows a poor relationship between the gods and mortals.

The story begins with Zeus walking on the Earth and catching sight of Callisto, a young woman who had pledged herself to Artemis, the Goddess of the Hunt. Of course, part of the pledge was to remain a virgin, but Zeus saw to it that this was broken. Distraught, Callisto returned to Artemis' entourage of young women, but her personality was now introverted and less outgoing. She was able to hide her pregnancy until just prior to the birth of her son Arco. She was then banished from Artemis' group, but the child was spared. Hera, Zeus' jealous wife, tracked down Callisto and turned her into a bear to roam the forest.

As time passed, Arco grew into manhood and became a great hunter. One day while traveling through the forest, his mother recognized him, and in her joy rushed to hug him. The charging bear caused Arco to fire an arrow from his bow. At that moment Zeus intervened – he changed Arco into a bear, grabbed him and Callisto by their tails, and slung them into the heavens. In the process, their tails were greatly stretched, which is outlined by the stars.

The story does not end here, though, for Hera is still outraged that one of Zeus' mistresses has been glorified by being placed in the heavens. In spite, she lowered the horizon of the Earth so that in the course of their daily circuit around the North Pole, neither bear reaches the ocean's waters to cool their paws.

The last aspect of the myth demonstrates that these two are technically Circumpolar Constellations, for they can be seen year round. I have included these two in the Spring Constellations since Ursa Major is so dominant in the sky during this season and because it can be used to locate several Spring Constellations – **Bootes**, **Hercules**, and **Leo**.

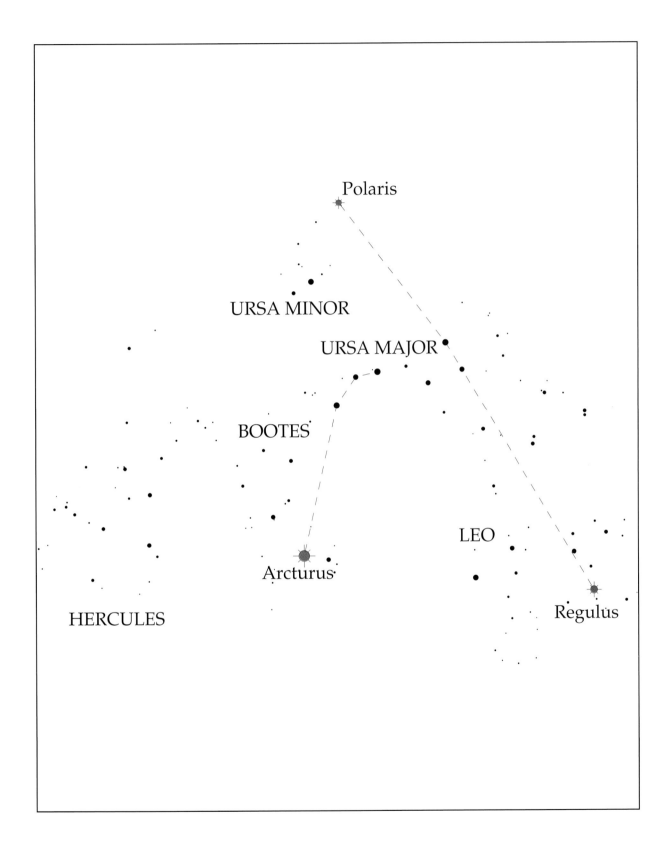

Polaris

URSA MINOR

URSA MAJOR

BOOTES

LEO

Arcturus

HERCULES

Regulus

Ursa Major (The Big Dipper)

As you orient yourself, face due North so that the sunset was on your left. The Big Dipper consists of the seven equally-bright stars high in the sky. The dipper, however, is upside down during the Spring. The handle of the dipper is the tail of the bear. The four cup stars make up part of the Great Bear's back. At dark locations, fainter stars depicting the paws can be seen. By the way, many other civilizations do not see a dipper. In Great Britain it is a plow. Another description is the three handle stars are horses pulling a stagecoach (the cup). In particular, the middle star in the handle, the one where the bend occurs, has been called Jack and the Horse, for there is a faint star near the brighter one. Native Americans used this pair of stars, named Alcor and Mizar, as an eyesight test.

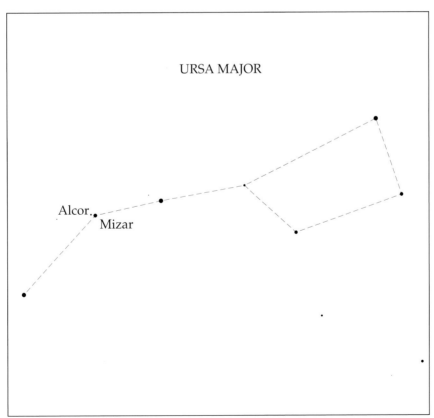

URSA MAJOR

Alcor.

Mizar

Ursa Minor (The Little Dipper)

To find Ursa Minor, go back to The Big Dipper. The two stars at the far end of the Dipper's cup are the Pointer stars, for they point to Polaris, the Pole Star. Begin at the bottom of the cup and go about five times the distance of the separation of the two stars. Polaris' position is extremely close to where the Earth's North Pole projects on the sky. Or another way to put it, if you stood on the North Pole and looked straight up, Polaris would be overhead. All the northern hemisphere stars appear to rotate around Polaris each night.

Polaris is the tip of the tail of Ursa Minor. Unfortunately, Ursa Minor is much fainter than Ursa Major. Besides Polaris, only the two corresponding pointer stars are bright. A dark location is necessary to make out the stars in between. You should notice that the handle of the Little Dipper bends up, while that of the Big Dipper bends down. During the night as the sky rotates, these two dippers pour into each other.

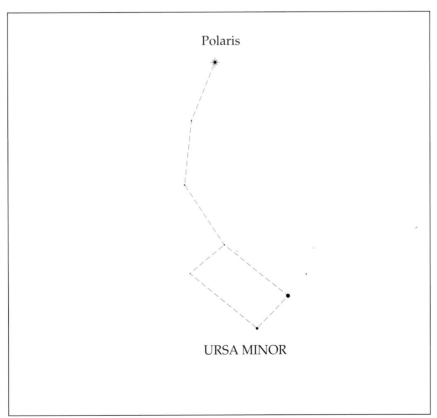

Polaris

URSA MINOR

Bootes

Earlier we used the cup of the Big Dipper, and now it is time to use the handle. Start near the cup and extend the arc of the handle to a bright star. The expression is "follow the arc to Arcturus." Arcturus is the brightest star in Bootes the Herdsman. (Bootes is pronounced "booties.") It is pretty difficult to readily make out the figure of a man, but Bootes does resemble two other common objects – an ice cream cone or a kite, take your pick. For either one, Arcturus is at the bottom of a long, narrow V (the cone). A few stars near the top of the cone form the ice cream, and several others near Arcturus represent the melting, dripping ice cream. Likewise, using these same stars, Arcturus is at the bottom of the kite. I tend to see the kite when Bootes is low on the horizon and the ice cream cone when it is more overhead.

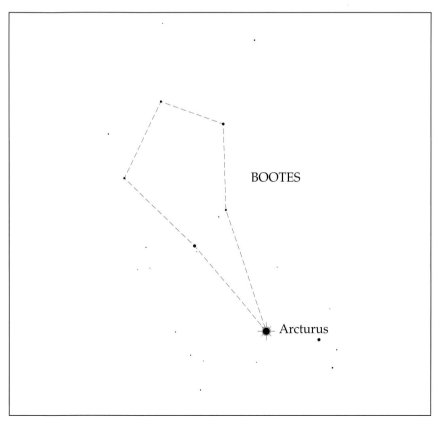

Hercules

Another giant man in the sky is Hercules, and just about everyone has heard of the twelve labors he endured. Some astronomers and historians suggest that all twelve of the labors are depicted in the heavens. For example, Leo is the lion he killed and nearby Bootes is actually Atlas, who holds up the world. Hercules is about as visible as Bootes, except it does not have a bright star like Arcturus. The notable shape is a keystone that represents his body, and off of each corner is an arm or leg. Hercules is depicted upside-down.

The diagram indicates the location of the M13 globular star cluster. This is one of the few such clusters that can barely be seen with the naked eye. These types of objects are described in the chapter *Faint, Diffuse Objects*.

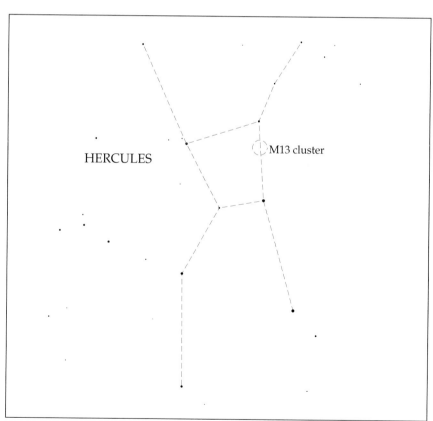

HERCULES

M13 cluster

Leo

I have saved a grand, or shall I say regal, constellation for last – Leo the Lion, which, yes, is redundant. You should face the South with the sunset to your right. Brilliant Orion is on the Western horizon, sinking away. On the meridian is Leo, and although its stars are not quite as bright as those in the Big Dipper, it is the largest and brightest of the Spring Constellations. You can use the Big Dipper to confirm it is indeed Leo. The Lion is below the pan of the cup, as if someone was trying to swat the cat (which I do not wish being done to any kitty).

Leo looks exactly like a cat sitting on the floor. The brightest star, Regulus, is at the bottom of a backwards question mark. This question mark is the Lion's head, and Regulus is the front shoulder. To the left of the question mark you will see three stars that outline the back and belly. Then several more stars curve back underneath the belly to form his tail. Leo has a forepaw to the right of Regulus.

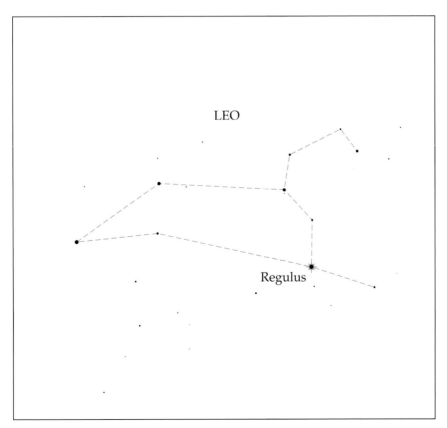

LEO

Regulus

Summer Constellations

The bright stars that form the Summer Triangle highlight the Summer Constellations. All three, though, are in different constellations – Deneb is in **Cygnus**, Vega shines in **Lyra**, and Altair graces **Aquila**. There are two other big, bright, and beautiful Summer Constellations, **Scorpius** and **Sagittarius**, but they are significantly far to the South, so you must have a clear horizon or live in the Southern tier of states to see them well. A compact constellation called **Delphinus** is also described.

The Milky Way band deserves a short mention here for it is most prominent during the Summer months. The surest way to identify it is by Cygnus, since the long neck of the Swan lies in the Milky Way. The brightest part of the band is down in the area of Sagittarius. To try to see the Milky Way, you must be in a very dark location and the Moon cannot be up.

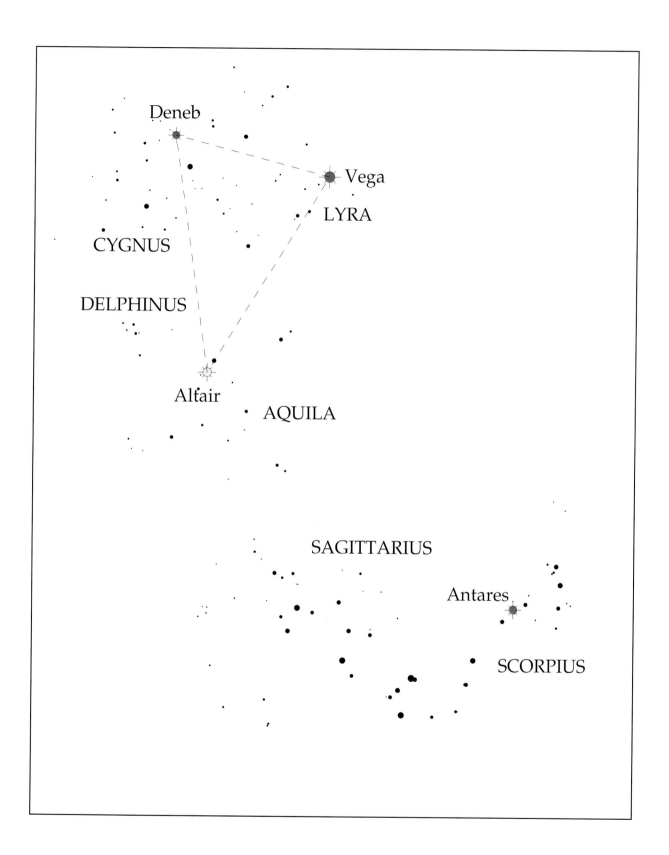

Cygnus

Cygnus looks like a large cross. The star farthest to the North is Deneb, one of the Summer Triangle stars, and it is at the head of five or six stars that form the Northern Cross. This, however, is not the constellation proper. Take the six stars that make the cross and reverse the orientation. Now the foot of the cross is the head of Cygnus the Swan. It has its long neck and outstretched wings, as shown by the horizontal cross bar. The bright star Deneb is the Swan's rump.

There are several myths about Cygnus, but the one I prefer begins with the story of Phaethon. He was the boy who asked his father to let him drive the Sun chariot across the sky. But Phaethon was not able to control the horses, and because the chariot was running wildly and endangering the Earth, Zeus killed the lad with a lightning bolt. Phaethon's charred body fell from the sky into a deep lake. His close friend Cycnus wanted to give Phaethon a proper burial. He had to dive deeply into the water many times to bring up the individual bones. After completing this task, for his love and dedication, Zeus rewarded the boy Cycnus by turning him into the swan Cygnus.

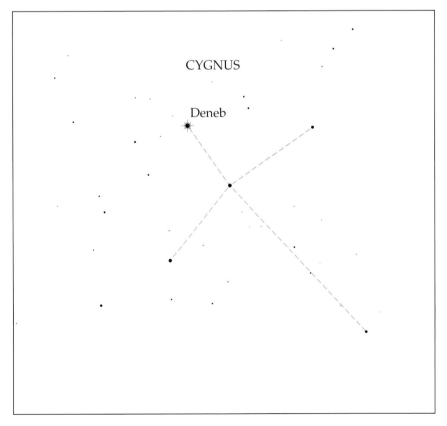

CYGNUS

Deneb

Lyra

The second constellation contains the brightest star of the Summer Triangle. The star is Vega, and it is in Lyra, the Small Harp or Lyre. Near Vega you will see four fainter, but equally bright, stars that form a parallelogram. The long sides of the parallelogram represent the strings of the harp. Vega is at the top of the instrument, and it is not too difficult imagining the outline of a harp with a few faint stars.

This lyre belonged to Orpheus, whose skill with it was so great that even arrows in flight would be swayed by his music. A poisonous snake bit his wife Eurydice on their wedding day, and he went to Hades to recover her. But on his way back out, he broke his pledge to Pluto, ruler of the underworld, of not looking back at her until they were out of Hades. After his return and without his bride, he roamed the world telling all of his grief. With his sad music, many young women were touched by his plight. Later they became angry by his rejections. Eventually, they were so enraged that they attempted to kill him. All of their weapons failed to hurt Orpheus, until the women's loud shrieks drowned out his music, and then they stabbed him to death. Zeus recovered Orpheus' lyre and placed it in the sky.

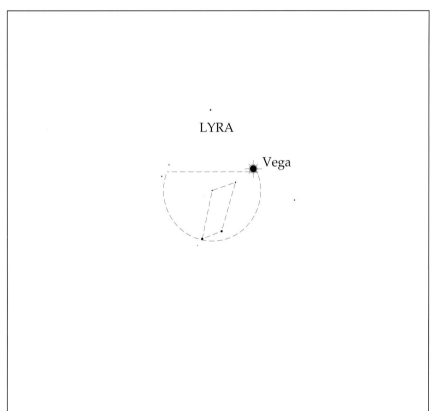

LYRA

Vega

Aquila

The third star of the Summer Triangle, Altair, is much farther South than Deneb and Vega. Unlike the other two constellations, Aquila the Eagle, looks like nothing recognizable. Even I cannot give you a good description to help visualize a bird. The most prominent feature is Altair and two other nearby stars that together form a "bent twig" shape.

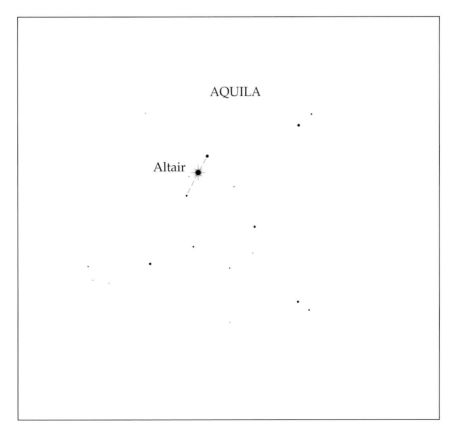

AQUILA

Altair

Scorpius

Scorpius looks exactly like a scorpion – it even has a red star, Antares, for its heart. The stinger is very clear, and its circle of stars surrounds a rather dark area on the sky. The ancient Greeks believed this region was the portal to Hades through which Orpheus entered. According to one myth, the Scorpion killed Orion.

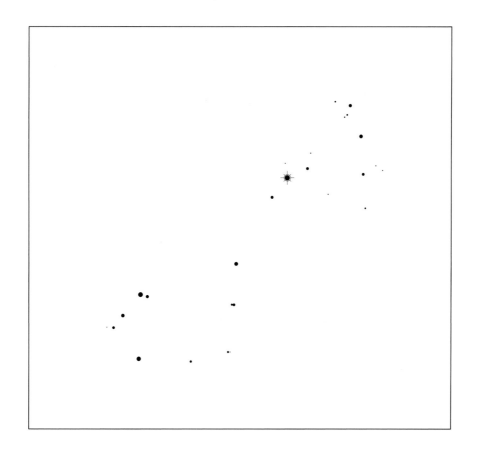

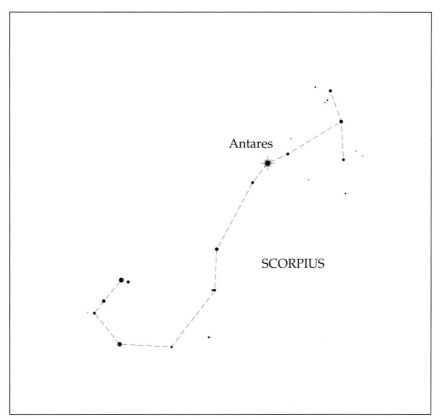

Antares

SCORPIUS

Sagittarius

To keep Scorpius under control, Sagittarius the Archer has an arrow aimed directly at its red heart. Sagittarius is a centaur, a being with the upper torso of a man and the body of a horse. The actual arrangement of stars has the shape of a teapot. Nearby are a lemon wedge and sugar spoon. A few stars depict the fire underneath the pot, and the diffuse Milky Way illustrates the escaping steam from the boiling water.

Like M13 in Hercules, M22 is a just-barely-detectable globular cluster. Sagittarius is also the region of the sky toward the center of our Galaxy, and the Milky Way band is bright in this direction. See the chapter *Faint, Diffuse Objects* for more information about these objects.

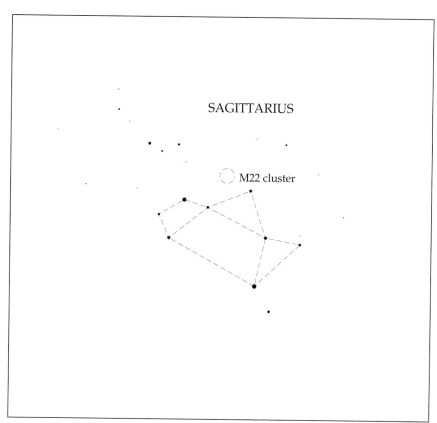

SAGITTARIUS

M22 cluster

Delphinus

Delphinus the Dolphin is a small constellation but a delight to see. A dolphin was placed in the sky by Zeus because of their love toward and help for sailors adrift. Delphinus "swims" underneath the Milky Way and is depicted as jumping out of the water.

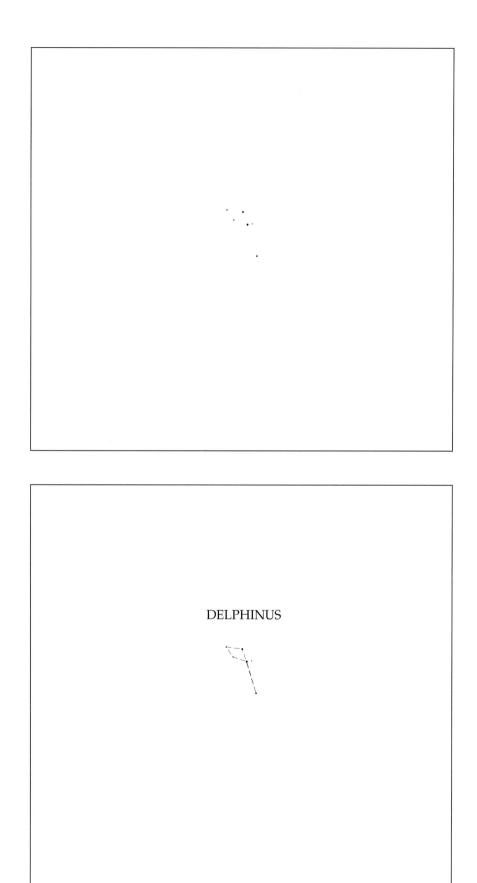

DELPHINUS

Autumn Constellations

The Autumn Constellations are bound together by a well-known myth. The key players are **Cassiopeia** the Queen, **Cepheus** the King, **Andromeda** the daughter, **Perseus** the hero, **Pegasus** the winged horse, and **Cetus** the sea monster. (Cetus is a very faint constellation and is not described below). Let me tell you the story before we learn the constellations.

Cepheus and Cassiopeia were the rulers of Ethiopia. Cassiopeia was rather vain, and one day boasted her beauty was greater than that of the Water Nymphs. Of course, they ultimately heard of this boast, and, being so enraged, complained to their father Poseidon to avenge them. He obliged by sending the sea monster Cetus to terrorize the country. Cepheus had the good sense to seek counsel from an oracle, who explained the situation. Unfortunately, the appeasement would be the sacrifice of their daughter Andromeda to the sea monster. Sadly, Cepheus and Cassiopeia had her chained to the rocks near the water's edge and waited for Cetus to devour her.

Meanwhile, a young man by the name of Perseus had been dealing with his own problems. His father was Zeus and his mortal mother was Danae. His grandfather had been foretold that Danae's son would kill him, so when she became pregnant, he cast her out to sea. But she survived and Perseus grew to be a strong young man. To save his mother, who had recently become a slave, he journeyed to find and kill the Gorgon Medusa. This creature was described as the most hideous being, for if you laid eyes on her you would turn to stone. It was said that she had snakes on her head instead of hair. Perseus was helped by the goddess Minerva and used a highly polished shield to "see" the reflection of Medusa. He cut off her head and put it in a bag. One version of the story claims Pegasus, a winged horse, sprang forth from her body when the head was severed. Perseus took the bag with Medusa's head and flew off on Pegasus' back.

During this trip, Perseus saw Andromeda chained to the rocks. He showed Medusa's head to the sea monster, and it immediately turned to stone. Perseus saved the day and got Andromeda as his wife (and ultimately the Kingdom of Ethiopia). Then Perseus returned to his homeland, where he rescued his mother by purposely revealing Medusa to many of his enemies. Later, he accidentally killed his grandfather with a discus, thus fulfilling the prophesy.

Not a bad story. But why were Cepheus and Cassiopeia, in particular, glorified with placement in the heavens? Actually, they are being punished. As you will soon see, these two constellations are Circumpolar, like Ursa Major and Ursa Minor in the Spring, so they never set. Both the King and Queen must suffer the indignity of being turned upside-down each night and must struggle to hold onto their thrones.

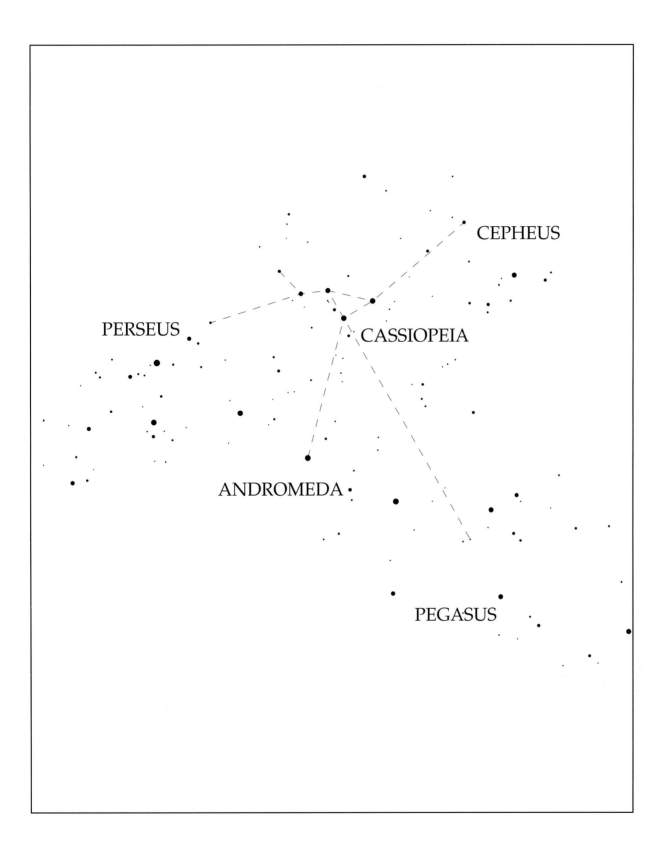

CEPHEUS

PERSEUS

CASSIOPEIA

ANDROMEDA

PEGASUS

Cassiopeia

Of all the Autumn Constellations mentioned, Cassiopeia the Queen is the brightest and easiest to recognize. Looking toward the North, she appears as a W or M depending on which side of the Celestial North Pole she is then on. This shape is a side view of her throne. There is a high back of the chair, the seat, and the front leg. I have to apply some creative imagination to make out the back leg. Then draped on the throne is the figure of Cassiopeia. There is not much of a body there, except for a bright star indicating her foot. Most people prefer to think the W shape represents a crown.

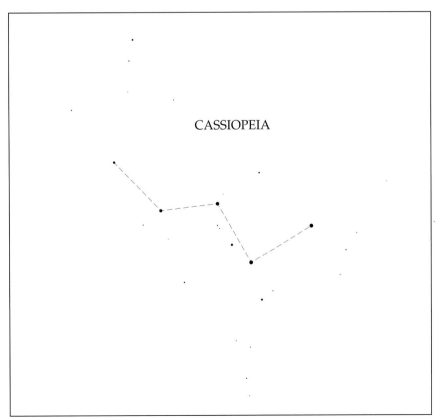

CASSIOPEIA

Cepheus

The two rightmost stars of the W-shaped Cassiopeia point toward Cepheus the King, which is a rather faint constellation. Its shape is a pentagon and at times is turned upside down. He is also sitting on a throne, only this time the view is straight on. The top of the pentagon is the back of the throne, the next stars down are the arms of the great chair, and the bottom stars are the legs.

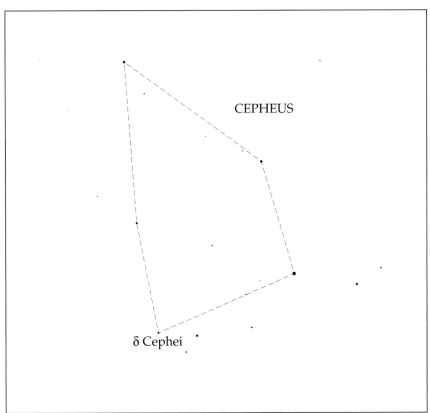

CEPHEUS

δ Cephei

Pegasus

Turning due East (or straight overhead later in the night) you will see a Great Square – this is the body of Pegasus the Winged Horse. Only the front half of the stallion is usually depicted on drawings, and he is actually upside down. On the star chart, the Winged Horse's head is connected to the lower right star of the square.

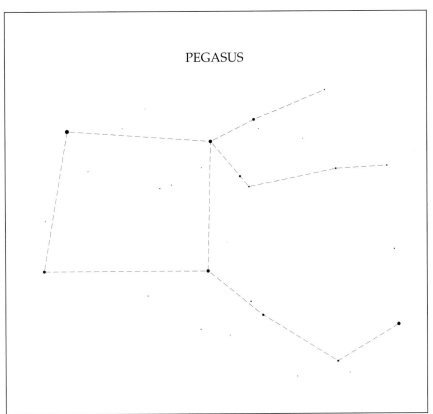

PEGASUS

Andromeda

Although the Andromeda constellation contains many stars, its diffuse shape makes it easy to overlook. Andromeda's head is the bottom left star of the "square of Pegasus." Several fainter stars below this one (that is, diagonally toward the upper left on the star chart) outline her chained body and loose dress blowing in the ocean breeze. As the constellation gets higher overhead, the Andromeda figure will appear more upright.

The M31 object, known as the *Andromeda Galaxy*, receives special attention at the very end of the book in *Faint, Diffuse Objects*.

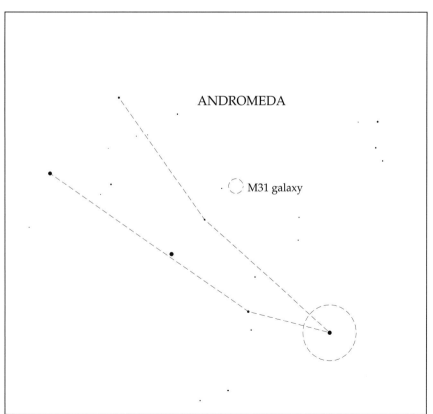

ANDROMEDA

M31 galaxy

Perseus

The shape of Perseus is a three-fingered claw. The handle is the upper body, and the two longer fingers are his legs. The third finger (on the left side as we view it) is smaller and more rounded; this outlines the small bag containing Medusa's head.

Open star clusters, two of which are depicted on the diagram, are different from globular clusters. The Pleiades and Hyades clusters in Taurus are excellent examples of open clusters. Several other such clusters are listed in *Faint, Diffuse Objects*.

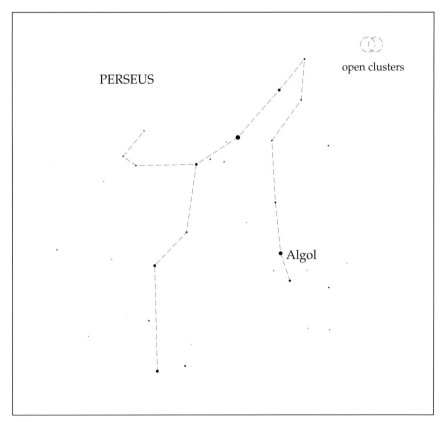

PERSEUS

open clusters

Algol

Zodiacal Constellations

Earlier when we examined the Seasons, we learned that the 23.5° tilt of the Earth's axis was the reason the Sun's position in the sky varied above and below the Celestial Equator. The path of the Sun against the background of stars is the **Ecliptic**, and the constellations through which it travels are called the **Zodiac**. These twelve constellations are well known because of the unfortunate popularity of astrology and horoscopes in today's culture. We, however, will examine the astronomy behind them. There are various theories as to the initial role of these constellations – suggestions include (a) maps for travelers, (b) calendars for farmers, and/or (c) religious stories for the people.

The Zodiacal Constellations are, in order on the sky, **Taurus** the Bull, **Gemini** the Twins, **Cancer** the Crab, **Leo** the Lion, **Virgo** the Virgin, **Libra** the Scales, **Scorpius** the Scorpion, **Sagittarius** the Archer, **Capricornus** the Sea Goat, **Aquarius** the Water Bearer, **Pisces** the Fishes, and **Aries** the Ram. Most have already been identified for you. The others are rather faint and difficult to see except in dark locations. Notice that they are primarily animals and the word "zoology," the study of animals, has the same root as "zodiac."

There are several key locations in the Zodiac Constellations. Pisces contains the point where the Ecliptic crosses the Celestial Equator from the South to the North: this is the **Vernal Equinox** and the start of Spring. The other intersection is the **Autumnal Equinox**, which is located in Virgo. Cancer and Capricornus are the Northern- and Southern-most points into which the Sun travels. If you look at an "old-style" globe, the **Tropic of Cancer** and **Tropic of Capricornus** are indicated at 23.5° north and south, respectively.

A note should be said about astrology, but first I have explain another motion of the Earth. Because the Moon's orbit does not lie in the Ecliptic (it is tilted by 5°), the Moon tugs on the Earth. The effect is the Earth wobbles slightly – in exactly the same way that a spinning top, when tapped on its side, wobbles in addition to its spin. The slow wobbling, called **precession**, causes the Earth's rotation axis to draw out a large circle on the sky. It takes about 26,000 years for one wobble! Currently, the Earth's northern axis points toward the star Polaris.

An astronomer is a scientist who studies the Universe; an astrologer believes and practices that the planets "influence" your life. Why is it that you may be called a Cancer or a Libra or an Aries? By definition your *Sun Sign* is the constellation that the Sun was in when you were born. Precession has had an effect on the Zodiac, and it shows a major difference between astronomy and astrology. First, to make the math easier, let's say that precession only takes 24,000 years. Second, it was about 2,000 years ago that the Zodiac was established. [At this time, there was no difference between an astronomer and an astrologer.] But because 2,000 years have elapsed since its establishment and 2,000 years divided by 24,000 years is 1/12, the Sun Signs have slipped by one constellation. In other words, the Sun was not in your Sun Sign constellation at the time of your birth. An astronomer can tell you where the Sun really was on a particular date, whereas the astrologers are stuck with an outdated setup.

Another complication is the way astronomers have divided the night sky into constellations. The widths of the constellations on the Ecliptic are not equal, so the actual amount of time the Sun spends in each one varies considerably. Also, the Sun and Ecliptic go through a thirteenth constellation, Ophiuchus the Serpent Holder.

STARS, PLANETS, AND MORE

STARS

Although the stars appear as points of light in the night sky, there are three distinguishing characteristics that the naked eye can detect. These characteristics are (1) brightness, (2) color, and (3) variability.

The brightness is the easiest to distinguish – some stars are faint, some are bright. If all stars had the same intrinsic luminosity, then the brightness would be an indication of distance, for the farther away the star is from the Earth, the fainter it would appear. Actually, though, there is an extremely large variation in intrinsic stellar luminosity. Most of the stars we see are not nearby. Instead, they are extremely luminous lighthouses, hundreds or thousands of light years away, whose energy output compensates for the large gulf of distance between us. As you look at these stars, you are looking back in time and seeing them the way they were hundreds or thousands of years ago.

The second characteristic the eye can detect is the star's color or tint. There are red, orange, yellow, white, and blue-white stars scattered across the night sky. Unlike brightness, color has a direct astrophysical link, for it is correlated to the temperature of the star's surface. Red and orange stars have the coolest surfaces – that statement may sound strange for the temperatures are hotter than 2,000 K (3,100 F). As surface temperatures increase, the color shifts from orange to yellow to white and ultimately to blue-white. In comparison, the Sun's surface temperature is 5,800 K (10,000 F). The highest surface temperature estimates are 25,000 K (45,000 F).

The third and final attribute one can observe for a handful of stars is variability in their brightness. Although most stars have a constant brightness, there are numerous types of "variable" stars, and the brightness change in some of these can be seen with the naked eye. There are many amateur astronomers who regularly monitor variable stars by eye, with or without binoculars or telescopes, and report their brightness observations. In particular, the premier organization is the American Association of Variable Star Observers (AAVSO). Its address is given in the References Section.

The next pages describe several of the most notable stars. But first, some nomenclature needs to be reviewed. (1) The first astronomer to catalog the stars according to brightness was Hipparchus around 140 BC. He placed the brightest stars in the "first magnitude" category. The next brightest set was the "second magnitude", and this continued down to the faintest, "sixth magnitude" set. This terminology has been maintained, although the scale has been extended in both directions. Just remember, when you see a magnitude number (usually ranging from 0 to 6 for naked-eye stars), the *smaller* the number, the *brighter* the star. (2) One of the units of distance astronomers use is the "light year". Even though it has the word "year" in it, this is a measure of distance – the distance that light travels in one year. As an example, if a star is ten light years away, it took the star's light ten years to reach us. Consequently, we are seeing the star the way it was ten years ago. [See the *Sizes and Distances* section for a review of the light year.]

Normal Stars and Their Constellations

Orion contains two bright stars that provide an excellent comparison of extremes. The first is **Rigel**, the bright blue star that represents one of Orion's knees. The other is diagonally opposite: **Betelgeuse**, a red star, is Orion's right shoulder. In fact the Arabic translation of Betelgeuse is "arm pit." Rigel's surface temperature is 12,000 K (21,100 F), whereas Betelgeuse's is only 3600 K (6,000 F). Other differences between these two stars are immense. Rigel has a mass 20 times that of the Sun but is only about twice as big. Betelgeuse has the same amount of mass as the Sun but has swelled its diameter to an enormous dimension. If you were to place the center of Betelgeuse at the center of our Solar System, not only would the Sun be engulfed, but so would the orbits of Mercury, Venus, Earth, and Mars. The diameter of Betelgeuse is 100 times that of the Sun. This class of stars is justifiably called the supergiants. Betelgeuse is also a variable star similar to Mira – see below. It changes its size by about 10% in a periodic fashion over a five-year period. Correspondingly, its brightness varies over this time period, too. Although the change is relatively small, the naked eye can perceive it easily. Rigel and Betelgeuse are about 800 and 500 light years distant, respectively, so they are both extremely luminous.

Sirius, the Dog Star, [in Canis Major] holds many titles of distinction. First, it is the brightest star in the night sky. [If you ever want to win a trivia contest, the brightest star *in the sky* is the Sun!] Sirius is one of the few stars that appears bright because it is relatively nearby, being the seventh closest star to the Sun. Its distance is only nine light years away. When you look at Sirius, you are seeing it the way it was nine years ago. Sirius also has the distinction of being the brightest binary (or double) star system. Binary stars are gravitationally bound to each other and orbit about a common center of mass. In the Sirius system, the faint companion is a "dead" type of star known as a **White Dwarf**. These objects are the remnant cores of stars similar to the Sun. Their size is about that of the Earth, but their mass is comparable to the Sun's. Consequently, their density is very high. One cubic centimeter, about the size of a sugar cube, has as much mass as does an African bull elephant. White dwarfs no longer generate light by thermonuclear reactions in their cores, but rather are glowing embers from residual heat, so their luminosities are much dimmer than normal stars. Sirius is 10,000 times brighter than its white dwarf companion.

Procyon [in Canis Minor] is another one of the three naked-eye stars that is both bright and nearby. It just happens Procyon is near to Sirius on the sky. [The third nearby, bright star is Alpha Centauri, but it cannot be seen from the continental United States due to its extreme southern location.] Procyon is only 11 light years away. Like Sirius, it is a binary system, and the fainter component is also a white dwarf.

Capella [in Auriga] is bright diamond in the sky. I find its appearance to be rather similar to that of Venus. Capella is a double star in which both components are almost exactly alike. These stars are more massive than, but have the same temperature as, our Sun.

Aldebaran [in Taurus] and **Antares** [in Scorpius] are both orange-red stars. They are not as large as Betelgeuse, being about 25 times larger than the Sun, so they are known as Red Giants. These two bright stars are close to the Ecliptic, and at times the Moon passes directly in front of them. Such an obscuration is called an *occultation*.

Deneb [in Cygnus] is another supergiant, but it is a hot blue one. Deneb is one of the farthest stars we see, being roughly 1400 light years away.

All of the previously described binary stars cannot be resolved by the naked eye. But this pair, **Alcor** and **Mizar** [in Ursa Major] are a *visual* double star, meaning that both are seen. The bright one, Mizar, is the middle star of the handle of the Big Dipper. Alcor is much fainter and is slightly toward the last star of the handle. Alcor and Mizar have been used as a test of eyesight by many civilizations. They have been referred to as Jack and the Horse. Because we can actually see both stars, they must be extremely distant from each other. The period for one complete orbit is several thousand years. Mizar itself is a visual double, but to see it "split" requires a pair of binoculars. In fact, in 1650, Mizar was the first binary star discovered.

Variable Stars

Algol [in Perseus], in 1669, was the first detected variable star. Algol keeps a constant brightness for about 2.9 days. Then it drops down in brightness and returns back up in just a few hours. In 1783 astronomers ascertained that Algol is not an intrinsic variable, for it does not pulsate. Rather, it is a binary star system whose orbit is edge-on to our line of sight. Regularly, one star moves in front of the second one every 2.9 days. This situation is reversed halfway through the period, but the secondary eclipse is not deep since the eclipsed star is very faint.

δ **Cephei** [in Cepheus] was the first intrinsic variable to be discovered (in 1784). This star is a supergiant like Betelgeuse but not as cool, so it has a yellow appearance. Due to the smaller size, the period of variability is shorter, being just 5.4 days. During one pulsation, δ Cephei's diameter increases and then decreases over a range of 20%. This star is the prototype for a very important class of variables called *Cepheids*. Because these stars seem to have similar characteristics and because they can be identified in nearby galaxies, they are used to estimate the size of the Universe!

Polaris [in Ursa Minor] is also a Cepheid. It has a period of just less than four days, and its change in brightness is about 10%.

Mira [in Cetus the Sea Monster] is one of the coolest and largest stars known. It has been estimated at 420 times the size of the Sun, so it is much larger than Betelgeuse. Usually, Mira is much fainter than the eye's detection limit, but about every 11 months it comes roaring into sight. Both the brightness range and period of Mira's variability are not constant.

PLANETS

Recognizing the planets in the night sky is a real treat. Being able to identify them creates a familiarity. You look up in the sky and there is one of your friends!

Several of the planets are brighter than most of the stars, so the recognition is usually easy. Once you know the constellation patterns, the identification of planets is simple. Either you see an extra "star" that does not belong in the constellation or, if you know which constellation the planet is in, you have a general idea of where to search for it. Because the planets have orbits in nearly the same plane as the Earth's, they are generally found along the Ecliptic in the Zodiacal Constellations.

All ancient civilizations identified five *wanderers* in the night sky: Mercury, Venus, Mars, Jupiter, and Saturn. In addition, there are currently two other planets – Uranus and Neptune. The motions of the planets fall into two categories, Inferior and Superior Planets, and we shall investigate these two types.

Mercury and Venus

Motions

Mercury and Venus are nearer to the Sun than the Earth, and for that reason they have the label **Inferior Planets**. Their smaller orbits cause them to stay on the Ecliptic near the Sun. These two are only seen for a couple of hours either right after sunset or right before sunrise. You cannot see either one at midnight.

The following diagram displays their orbits along with the Earth's. When a planet is exactly in line between the Sun and Earth, it is at **Inferior Conjunction**. **Superior Conjunction** is the planet's location on the Earth-Sun line when it is on the far side of the Sun. Although these two planets obviously tend to stay near the Sun on the sky, their angle (distance) from it varies. The maximum angle away is the planet's **Greatest Elongation**. For Venus, its Greatest Elongations are $47°$ whereas Mercury's are only $28°$. There are two elongations: in the evening the Sun sets in the West, so this maximum elongation is called the Greatest Eastern Elongation, for the planet has moved as far away as it will get from the Sun toward the Eastern horizon. The maximum elongations in the morning are Greatest Western Elongations.

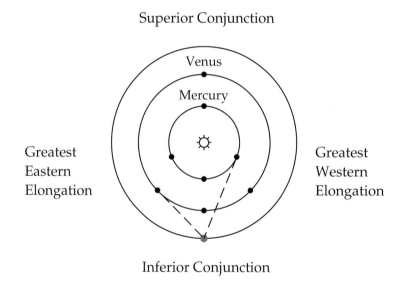

Superior Conjunction

Venus

Mercury

Greatest Eastern Elongation

Greatest Western Elongation

Inferior Conjunction

After the Sun and Moon, Venus is the brightest, most spectacular object in the sky – I liken its appearance to that of a diamond. Venus spends about seven months in the evening sky, disappears for about a week, and then reappears in the morning sky, where it stays again for seven months. When it disappears a second time (approaching Superior Conjunction), it is out of sight for several months. Because its orbit is relatively close in size to the Earth's, its orbital speed is not much faster than ours. When it is on the far side of the Sun, we are both moving around the Sun at about the same speed, so Venus remains behind the Sun and out of sight for a long time. Also, when Venus is visible, its motion on the sky toward and away from the Sun is not constant. Its angular speed is much faster when it is near the Earth, much slower as the separation increases.

Mercury is a very elusive planet to spot, even though at times it is brighter than Sirius. Mercury has a reddish tint and is always seen in the glare of twilight. Its close proximity to the Sun prevents us from seeing it except for about 10-day stretches when Mercury is near a greatest elongation. There is a story, though most astronomers find it hard to accept as truth, that Copernicus on his deathbed lamented he had never seen Mercury. [Copernicus, in 1543, was the first person to present a solid theory that the planets revolve around the Sun instead of the Earth.]

Although Mercury and Venus do not travel around the sky like the rest of the planets, only these two go through phases similar to those of the Moon. One needs a pair of binoculars to witness this. In the history of the development of science and our understanding of the workings of the heavens, Galileo's observations of the complete display of phases by Venus were the convincing, indisputable evidence that it orbited the Sun and not the Earth.

Descriptions

Mercury is a heavily cratered world a little bit bigger than our Moon. In many ways, it resembles the Moon except it lacks the dark mare (seas). Mercury's orbital period is 88 earth days, and it rotates in about 59 days. This combination is such that Mercury has three days (rotation) for every two years (revolution). Mercury has no atmosphere and no moons.

Venus has about the same size and mass of the Earth, but that is where the similarities end. A very thick atmosphere consisting primarily of carbon dioxide dominates Venus' surface. Its atmosphere extends up to about 40 miles (70 km), whereas the Earth's lowest, main layer only reaches about six miles in height. The pressure at the surface of Venus is almost 90 times that of sea level, and the temperature is about 480 C (900 F) – it is actually hotter than the surface of Mercury. Within the atmosphere is a 12 mile (20 km) thick layer of clouds that completely surrounds the planet. These clouds are what make Venus so reflective and bright. It is believed that a runaway green-house effect created the thick atmosphere and may have even evaporated theorized ancient oceans. Venus has no moon.

Mars, Jupiter, and Saturn

Motions

Because Mars, Jupiter, and Saturn have larger orbits than the Earth's, they are known as **Superior Planets**. Their farther orbits make it possible for them to be seen anywhere along the Ecliptic. Depending upon their orbital positions, they can be seen at any time of the night and at any angle away from the Sun. These three do not experience the phase changes as do Venus and Mercury, for their appearances are always near "full." They do have significant brightness variations, though, because of their large changes in distance from the Earth. Mars has a reddish tint, Jupiter glows white like a pearl, and Saturn has a yellowish hue.

The diagram below shows the orbits of the Earth, Mars, Jupiter, and Saturn to scale. When the superior planets are on the other side of the Sun on the Earth-Sun line, they are at **Conjunction**. **Opposition** is the location directly opposite from the Sun as seen from the Earth. This is the time of the planet's closest approach to us.

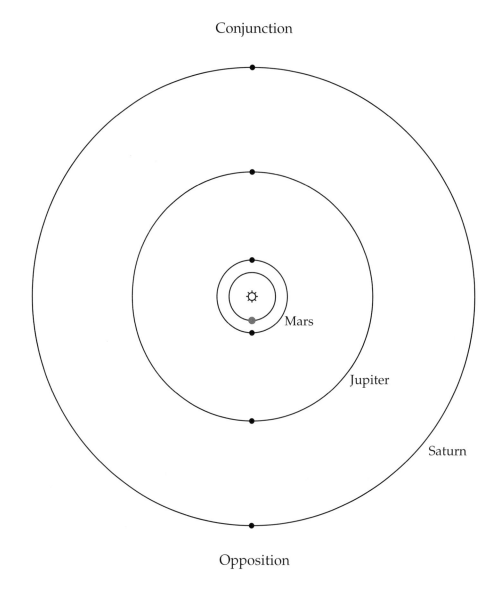

Conjunction

Mars

Jupiter

Saturn

Opposition

At first, one would rightly think the motion of these planets would be uniform and constant across the sky. After all, with respect to the stars they are always moving counterclockwise around the Sun. However, as seen from the Earth, each one periodically reverses its direction on the sky for days to months! Later, they change directions again and proceed on as if nothing has happened. A prescribed number of months later, the reversal occurs again.

Nothing has altered their regular orbits as viewed from above the Solar System. Their **Retrograde Motion** is an observational phenomenon due to the Earth's motion around the Sun. The nearer a planet is to the Sun, the faster its orbital speed. For example, as the Earth catches up with Mars near opposition, the Earth's faster speed means it travels a greater distance in the same amount of time. Against the distant stars, Mars appears to move backwards, even though it has not changed its motion. [The same phenomenon is seen with cars driving on the highway. As a faster car approaches and overtakes a slower one, the slower car appears to be moving backwards against the distant terrain.]

Descriptions

Mars has a little of everything, and in many ways is similar and simpler than the Earth. It does not have the canals that Percival Lowell claimed in the late 1890s, but it does have both common and unique surface features. Common features are craters, mountains, and smooth plains. The unique ones include several extremely large volcanoes – Olympus Mons is 16 miles (27 km) high whereas Mt. Everest is about six miles high. Valles Marineris is a giant canyon as wide as Tennessee and stretches the length of the continental United States. Mars does have some water, but it is in the form of ice (primarily in the polar caps), frost, and (probably) permafrost. There is no liquid water on the surface, but dried riverbeds have been identified. The reddish color of the surface is due to the rocks and dirt being highly oxidized or rusted. Mars has two small moons, **Phobos** and **Deimos**, which mean *fear* and *panic*.

Jupiter and Saturn, along with Uranus and Neptune, are quite different from the hard, rocky terrestrial planets, Mercury, Venus, Earth, and Mars. Rather, these giant worlds are primarily gaseous. There are no hard surfaces, just gas clouds that extend down to the core. Jupiter is the largest and most massive planet in the Solar System. It is also the fastest rotator, for one day is just under ten hours! This rapid rotation causes it to be slightly flattened, and it stretches the weather patterns (winds) into long continuous bands. Consequently, Jupiter has a striped appearance when seen through a small telescope or pair of binoculars. Although it has at least 49 moons, **Io**, **Europa**, **Ganymede**, and **Callisto** (known as the Galilean moons since he discovered them) are the largest and most interesting ones. To begin with, these moons are about half rock and half ice, unlike our Moon which is all rock. Io has active volcanoes whereas nearby Europa is completely covered with a thick layer of ice that apparently rides on top of a 60-mile (100 km) deep ocean! Ganymede is larger than the planet Mercury, and Callisto is covered with craters.

Saturn is best known for its rings. Without them, it would be a rather dull, yellowish world, whose stripes are much less distinct than Jupiter's. But the rings make it one of the most memorable views in the night sky, although a small telescope is required. The rings are not continuous sheets of material but are instead made up of billions of tiny particles, each in orbit about Saturn as a moon. The particles range in size from snowflakes, to baseballs, to a few trashcan-sized pieces. However, the rings are only about ten yards (ten meters) thick! Saturn has 53 known moons, and the largest one, **Titan**, is shrouded in an orange gaseous atmosphere.

Uranus and Neptune

Motion

These superior planets are not naked-eye objects, although Uranus can just barely be seen at a very dark site. If they could be observed with the naked-eye, they would behave as the other superior planets.

Description

Uranus is about five times the size of the Earth. It is the plainest of all the planets, for its cloud-covered surface is a very uniform pale-green color. Uranus' most unique characteristic is its axis of rotation being tilted by more than $90°$. To understand how this orientation affects its seasons, think of a rotisserie chicken. During one season, the Sun shines on only the north-pole region. In the next season the entire planet is illuminated. In the third season the southern hemisphere is illuminated, and this is followed by the entire planet again receiving light in the fourth season. Uranus has ten faint, tenuous rings and about 27 moons.

Neptune is similar to Uranus in size and composition. It has a deeper blue color and does have the storms that Uranus lacks. Although Uranus was discovered by accident in 1781 by William Herschel, the discovery of Neptune was actually predicted. By 1844, astronomers could tell that the orbital motion of Uranus was perturbed and that another planet probably existed out beyond its orbit. Urbain Jean Joseph Leverrier in France and John Couch Adams in England independently predicted the location of Neptune, and they had almost identical positions for it. In 1846, Johann Gottfried Galle (in Germany) was the first to observe Neptune with a telescope, using the information from Leverrier. Neptune has a few partial rings – called *ringlets* – and at least 13 moons. **Triton** is an icy moon about the size of ours. Voyager photographs captured a few active *geysers* (not really volcanoes) on it and revealed a very thin atmosphere.

COMETS, METEORS, AND METEOR SHOWERS

Comets

The Solar System began as a giant, spherical cloud of gas and dust particles before collapsing to a disk and ultimately forming the planets, moons, and asteroids. The comets were formed while the cloud was still spherical. How do we know? The orbits of comets are randomly distributed and are not restricted to the Ecliptic. Consequently, comets are the oldest objects in the Solar System. Of particular interest is their composition, for it could tell us about the early Solar System.

What is a comet? The best description is a "dirty snowball" or "snowy dirtball" – lots of ices and a little bit of rock. Most comets are believed to be a few miles across. [Comet Hale-Bopp (in 1996) was very large, perhaps 25 miles in diameter. Its great size, and consequently higher reflectivity, is why it was discovered at a much larger distance than most other comets are first spotted.]

What does a comet look like? As the comet's highly elliptical orbit brings it near the Sun, some of its ices evaporate, forming the comet's **coma**. This spherical, fuzzy cloud is generally tens of thousands of miles in size and is highly reflective. The coma obscures our view of the **nucleus**, the "dirty snowball." Some of the comet's gas and dust are pushed away by the solar wind, an ejected stream of tiny, high-speed particles. This extension of the coma is the comet's tail. There are two **tails**, one composed of gases and the other consisting of dust.

The two tails behave differently during the comet's close encounter with the Sun. The gas tail always points away from the Sun, whereas the dust tail becomes rather curved and lags behind. The tails are generally millions of miles long and can extend for many degrees across the sky. [Remember the diameter of the Full Moon is half a degree.]

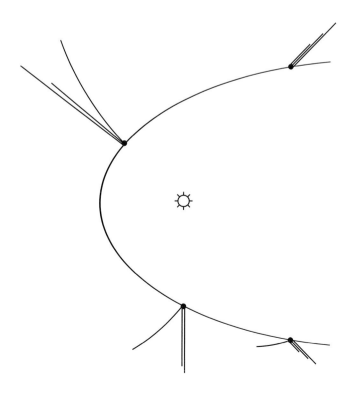

This picture of Comet Hale-Bopp shows the bright, curved dust tail and the narrow, straight, bluish gas tail. To the upper right is part of the Cassiopeia W shape, and the dash on the left is due to an airplane during the 10-second exposure.
(Photograph was taken by the author on March 27, 1997, north of Atlanta, GA.)

Meteors

Actually, in this section we will cover **Asteroids**, **Meteoroids**, **Meteors**, and **Meteorites**. Asteroids and meteoroids are rocky debris that were never assimilated into the Sun, a planet, or a moon. Asteroids are in the disk of the Solar System and most are found between Mars and Jupiter, but some have orbits that cross, or are completely inside, the Earth's orbit. Asteroids and meteoroids are not as old as comets, but they are still very primitive and have gone through little or no changes (such as melting), unlike the rocks of the Earth.

The only difference between asteroids and meteoroids is their size. Asteroids are the larger ones, ranging in the tens to hundreds of miles in diameter. Meteoroids are much smaller being under 100 yards across. Where is the dividing line? That determination is up to the individual – it is purely semantics. An object a quarter of a mile across is rather small for an asteroid, but if it were near the Earth, it would be considered a gigantic meteoroid.

Hitting the Earth is an important point as several Hollywood movies can attest. Millions of meteoroids are in orbit around the Sun. When one enters the Earth's atmosphere, the friction between it and the air causes part of the rocky meteoroid to heat up rapidly and vaporize. The vapor-trail streak across the sky is called a **Meteor**. This display also goes by the names "Shooting Star" or "Falling Star".

If a fragment of the meteoroid survives its flight through the atmosphere and lands with a thump on the Earth's surface, one now has a **Meteorite**. There are two ways to discover one. The first is to watch a meteoroid fall through the sky as a meteor and see it land. You then run over and pick it up, but watch out, it might be hot! You have just recovered a *Fall*. The second method is to get up one morning and notice a rock smashed in the hood of your car. You did not see it fall but you did *Find* a meteorite. [If it turns out that your rock is not extra-terrestrial, you then have a "meteor-wrong"!]

The composition of meteorites seems to fall [no pun intended] into two main categories. The first set is the **Irons**, for the composition is primarily iron and nickel. These rocks are heavier than typical terrestrial rocks, and you might be able to see solidified flow marks from melting during its travel through the atmosphere. The other major category is called **Stones**. As the name implies, these are more similar to terrestrial rocks. In fact, these are usually only found as Falls, because after a few years of weathering from rain and wind, they will lose their extra-terrestrial appearance. [By the way, most meteorites are found today by scientists traversing Antarctica with snowmobiles. Because the ice is a mile thick, any rock found at the surface must have come from the sky.]

There are rarer classes of meteorites, and these objects are useful to scientists. If you find a meteorite, please allow a scientist to analyze a small fragment before you put it in a drawer, donate it to a museum, or sell it to an entrepreneur. There might be a great discovery waiting to be found because of your contribution.

Meteor Showers

Contrary to their name, **Meteor Showers** are the result of comets. Remember that comets are in highly elliptical orbits. As one approaches the Sun, the heat and radiation cause the comet's ices to melt and geysers to form. The geysers eject gas and dust particles, creating the long, beautiful tails. The ejected particles remain in the comet's orbit, leaving behind a highly littered trail.

Some cometary orbits intersect the Earth's. Our planet revolves around the Sun at a speed of 20 miles per second (30 km/s). The meteor shower streaks are due to dust particles burning up as they hit the Earth's atmosphere. Because the comet orbits are fixed relative to the stars, the date of the Earth's passage through the debris field is the same each year. For example, the Perseid Meteor Shower is the result of Comet Swift-Tuttle, and the dates are from about August 11 to 13.

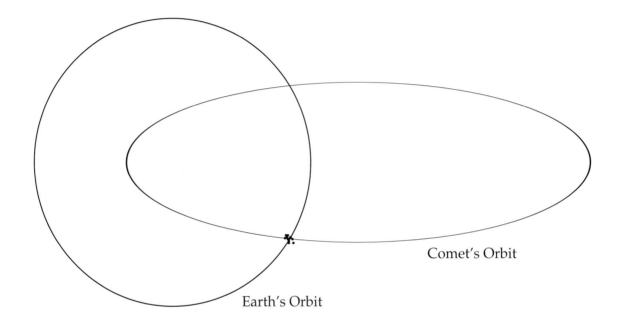

Comet's Orbit

Earth's Orbit

The best time to see a meteor shower is from about 3 am until morning twilight. The reasoning is demonstrated by the following analogy. Picture a car driving through a steady rainfall. The front windshield faces the direction the car is traveling, and it gets very wet from numerous raindrop hits. On the other hand, the rear window gets little if any rain, for it is pointed in the direction opposite to the car's motion.

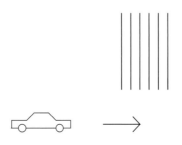

The Earth is revolving around the Sun and rotating on its axis. In the diagram below, both of these motions are counterclockwise. It is at about 6 am that the Earth faces the direction in the sky it is moving. But because the Sun has probably risen by then, we back up the optimal viewing time to about 3 am, while it is still very dark.

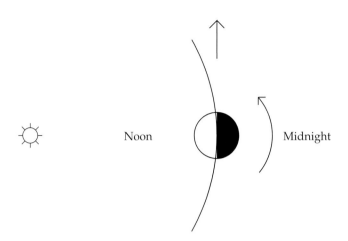

Noon   Midnight

From our vantage on the Earth, we see the debris field in front of the background stars. All of the streaks will appear to emanate from a particular location on the sky (i.e., a constellation). Meteor showers are named for the constellation that the streaks point back toward.

How many streaks should one see? The average for the Perseid Meteor Shower, often considered to be the best, is about one every minute or two. [In the table below, the "Rate" is the average number of streaks seen per hour.] However, several years ago as many as five per minute were seen in some parts of the world. On rare occasions, about once a century, lucky viewers witness a Meteor Storm – thousands of meteors per second!

Shower	Date	Rate
Quadrantids	Jan 3	40
Lyrids	Apr 21	15
Eta Aquarids	May 4	30
Perseids	Aug 11	50
Orionids	Oct 20	20
Leonids	Nov 16	12
Geminids	Dec 13	50

What is the best way to watch a meteor shower? First, no telescopes or binoculars are needed, just use your eyes. Second, find a location that has few obstructions, such as no trees or buildings, for you need to see as much of the sky as you can. Third, get to as dark a site as possible, for the darker the location, the better the chance of seeing the fainter streaks. Fourth, get a blanket, sleeping bag, or lawn chair to recline on. Now relax, lay back, and look straight up. Be patient – you will soon be rewarded with sightings you will never forget!

FAINT, DIFFUSE OBJECTS

The last set of objects we examine in this guide are visible to the naked eye, but they are difficult to initially detect. As you will see [pun intended] there is a wide assortment of celestial wonders waiting for you to gaze upon.

Star Clusters

Stars have a birth, life, and death. Their birth occurs in a large cloud of gas and dust, and hundreds or thousands of stars are formed at a time. Then ultraviolet radiation pressure and particle "winds" from the hottest, brightest, newly formed stars blow away the remaining gas and dust. Clusters are extremely important objects for the study of stellar evolution and for distance calibrations. There are two types of clusters, open and globular.

Open Clusters

Open clusters, such as the very familiar Winter-sky Pleiades cluster, contain young, massive, hot stars. Several such clusters appear large on the sky because they are relatively close to us. Open clusters are found in the spiral arms of our Galaxy, so most are seen on the sky near the Milky Way band. These clusters have several hundred members, but there is not enough mass and gravity to prevent the dispersion of the members with time. More than a thousand open clusters have been catalogued. The most prominent, naked-eye open clusters are listed in the following table.

Cluster	Constellation	Season
Pleiades	Taurus	Winter
Hyades	Taurus	Winter
h & χ Persei	Perseus	Autumn
Praesepe	Cancer	Summer
Coma Berenices	Coma Berenices	Spring

Globular Clusters

Globular Clusters contain many thousands of stars. These clusters are gravitationally bound and are not dispersed, so they end up having a somewhat spherical shape. The approximately 125 known globular clusters are extremely old objects. They are rather far away, forming a halo around the center of the Milky Way Galaxy. Consequently, many of these clusters are seen in Sagittarius and Scorpius.

Spotting a globular cluster without optical aid is a challenge. You will need a dark site and no Moon. They will appear as tiny, fuzzy, faint "clouds." A few of the brightest ones are listed below.

Cluster	Constellation	Season
	Northern Hemisphere	
M13	Hercules	Spring
M22	Sagittarius	Summer
	Southern Hemisphere	
Omega Centaurus	Centaurus	Spring

Gaseous Nebulae

There is a great deal of gas and dust in the Galaxy that is not tied up as stars or planets. This leftover material was too far from any star in a young open cluster to be gravitationally trapped. These gaseous nebulae have about 100 hydrogen atoms per every particle of dust. Although the densities are quite low – about one particle per cubic centimeter (the size of a sugar cube) – the extent of the nebula is huge. Often the hydrogen atoms are excited, and they de-excite by emitting a photon of light at a specific wavelength. Therefore, these are called Emission Nebulae.

The most conspicuous one is the Orion Nebula (M42). [You might want to refer back to the Orion description in the *Winter Constellation* section.] This nebula is a stellar nursery containing several hundred stars about 1400 light years away. Looking at the star chart for Orion, the most obvious feature is his belt. Below it are three other objects that form his sword, and the middle one is the Orion Nebula. You should notice it appears fuzzy and diffuse compared to the surrounding stars. [This is a case where *averted* vision is necessary to see it better. Averted vision is the technique or skill of looking slightly away from, instead of directly at, the faint celestial object. The sensitivity of the human eye is a little bit better slightly off-center than it is straight on.]

The Milky Way Galaxy

The Milky Way (or The Galaxy) is our concentration of some 200 billion stars. The Galaxy has a spiral shape with four arms, and we are believed to be in a spur that lies between two of them. We are about halfway out from the center, a distance of roughly 25,000 light years. The appearance of the Milky Way on the sky is that of a band. It is brightest in the Summer, for we are looking toward the galactic center, which lies in the direction of Sagittarius and Scorpius. The Winter's band is much fainter for now we are looking outward away from the center, and there are far fewer stars to produce the light.

With the naked eye one cannot resolve individual stars, but one can discern structure in the Milky Way. In the previous section it was mentioned that there are dust particles in the Gaseous Nebulae. Although this dust can produce a glow in the infrared, for visible observers it blocks light from more distant sources. There are substantial quantities of dust in the disk of the Galaxy, so much so that large rifts appear in the band; a large one is in Cygnus. A dark dust cloud, the Coal Sack, sits in an extremely bright section of the southern-hemisphere portion of the Milky Way.

Galaxies

There are trillions of other galaxies that make up the Universe. About half of them are spiral-shaped like ours, and the other half are typically elliptical or ball-shaped like globular clusters.

Galaxies tend to cluster together just as stars do. Our cluster is known as the Local Group, and the Milky Way and Andromeda Galaxy (another large spiral) dominate it. There are about two dozen smaller galaxies in the Local Group, and most of them form a close halo to either the Milky Way or Andromeda Galaxy. A few, though, are far enough out to be influenced by both.

The Large and Small Magellanic Clouds are two small satellite galaxies around the Milky Way. Ferdinand Magellan and his crew, upon completion of their circumnavigational trip in 1522, were the first to report the "clouds" to Europeans. These two galaxies are, unfortunately for us, very far South and cannot be seen from the continental United States. Southern-hemisphere observers, however, easily spot them. The Small Magellanic Cloud (SMC) appears circular and about the size of the Full Moon. The Large Magellanic Cloud (LMC) is about three times larger, and you can even make out an S-shaped appearance. You will not be able to resolve individual stars with the naked eye; rather, the appearance of these two is similar to the diffuse light of the Milky Way.

The Andromeda Galaxy (M31)[4] is the farthest object visible to the naked eye, being about 2 million light years away. It, too, will appear as a very faint, fuzzy patch in the constellation of Andromeda. The galaxy is easy to find with the help of stars from Cassiopeia and Andromeda. During Autumn, use the "top" three stars of Cassiopeia to form an arrow. Then go about two-thirds of the way to the bright arc of stars in Andromeda. It needs to be a moonless night with very little light pollution. The galaxy will be fuzzy, but a little brighter in the center.

When you view the Andromeda Galaxy, think of these words, "That light has been traveling for more than two million years for you to see it."

---

[4]It is object 31 in the Messier Catalog.

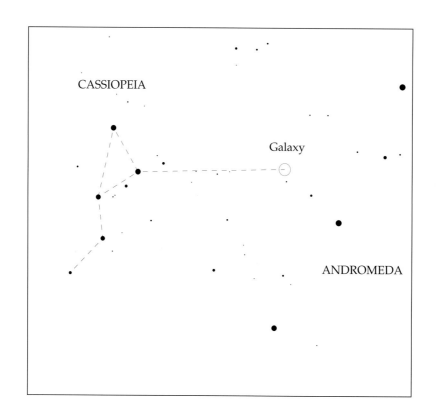

CASSIOPEIA

Galaxy

ANDROMEDA

EPILOGUE

I hope this guide has been an aid for you. My wish is that you will see many of the wonders and beauties of nature, the sky, and the Universe, and I hope that your appreciation, understanding, and excitement have been heightened.

APPENDICES

GLOSSARY

Aphelion The place in an object's orbit where it is farthest from the Sun.

Asteroid An object orbiting the Sun that is smaller than a planet. It shows no evidence of an atmosphere nor any type of activity associated with comets. Most asteroids are located between the orbits of Mars and Jupiter.

Autumnal Equinox The point of the Celestial Sphere where the Sun crosses the Celestial Equator passing from North to South (around September 23).

Black Hole A hypothetical body whose gravitational attraction is so strong that the escape velocity is greater than the speed of light, thus no light can leave it.

Blue Moon A second Full Moon in the same calendar month.

Brown Dwarf An object intermediate in mass between a planet and a star.

Celestial Equator The projection of the Earth's Equator onto the sky.

Celestial Poles The projection of the Earth's North and South Poles onto the sky.

Comet A small body of ice and dusty matter that revolves about the Sun. When a comet comes near the Sun, some of its material vaporizes, forming a large head of tenuous gas and often two tails.

Constellation A configuration of stars named for or depicting a particular object.

Ecliptic The apparent annual path of the Sun on the Celestial Sphere.

Equinox One of the intersections of the Ecliptic and the Celestial Equator. (See also Autumnal Equinox and Vernal Equinox.)

Galaxy A gravitationally-bound assemblage of millions to billions of stars.

Light Year The distance light travels in one year (about $6,000,000,000,000$ miles).

Lunar Eclipse The Moon moves into the shadow of the Earth.

Messier Catalog A list of 103 bright nebulous-like objects compiled by Charles Messier in 1781. This catalog includes gaseous nebulae, star clusters, and galaxies. Objects such as the Orion Nebula are referred to by the catalog's number, in this case as M42.

Meteor The luminous phenomenon observed when a meteoroid enters the Earth's atmosphere and burns up (a "shooting or falling star").

Meteor Shower Many meteors appearing to radiate from a common point in the sky caused by the collision of the Earth with a swarm of small dust particles blown off by a comet.

Meteorite A portion of a meteoroid that survives passage though the atmosphere and reaches the ground.

Meteoroid A particle in space before it encounters the Earth.

Milky Way The band of light encircling the sky, which is due to the many stars lying near the plane of our Galaxy.

Neutron Star A star of extremely high density, about ten miles in diameter, that is composed almost entirely of neutrons.

Obliquity The tilt of the rotational axis of a planet.

Perihelion The place in an object's orbit where it is closest to the Sun.

Planet Any of the eight largest bodies revolving about the Sun or any other similar non-self-luminous bodies that orbit other stars.

Pulsar A neutron star that emits radio pulses in very regular periods. The periods range from about 0.001 to 5 seconds.

Quasar A stellar-appearing object of very high speed, presumed to be a highly luminous galaxy.

Revolution The orbital motion of a body around a larger, more massive one.

Rotation The spin of a body around its own internal, central axis.

Solar Eclipse The passage of the Moon directly between the Earth and Sun.

Solstice Either of the two points on the Celestial Sphere where the Sun reaches its maximum distances North and South of the Celestial Equator.

Star A self-luminous sphere of gas that generates its luminosity via thermonuclear reactions.

Summer Solstice The point on the Celestial Sphere where the Sun reaches its greatest distance North of the Celestial Equator (around June 21).

Umbra The central, completely dark part of a shadow.

Universe The totality of space occupied by all matter and radiation.

Vernal Equinox The point of the Celestial Sphere where the Sun crosses the Celestial Equator passing from South to North (around March 20).

White Dwarf A star that has exhausted all of its nuclear fuel and has collapsed to about the size of the Earth.

Winter Solstice The point of the Celestial Sphere where the Sun reached its greatest distance South of the Celestial Sphere (around December 21).

Zodiac A band around the sky centered on the Ecliptic.

PLANETARY INFORMATION

Planet	Distance (AU)	Period (years)	Diameter (Earth=1)	Mass (Earth=1)	Rotation (days)	Tilt (deg)
Mercury	0.4	0.24	0.38	0.06	58.6	0
Venus	0.7	0.62	0.95	0.82	243	177.4
Earth	1.0	1.00	1.00	1.00	1.00	23.4
Mars	1.5	1.88	0.53	0.11	1.03	25.2
Jupiter	5.2	11.86	11.2	317.8	0.41	3.1
Saturn	9.5	29.46	9.41	94.3	0.43	26.7
Uranus	19.2	84.07	4.11	14.6	0.65	97.9
Neptune	30.1	164.82	3.81	17.2	0.72	29
Pluto	39.5	248.6	0.17	0.01	6.39	118

MOONS

Planet	Satellite	Discoverer	Date	Period (days)	Size (km)
Earth	Moon	——	——	27.32	3476
Mars	Phobos	Hall	1877	0.32	23
	Deimos	Hall	1877	1.26	13
Jupiter	Io	Galileo	1610	1.77	3630
	Europa	Galileo	1610	3.55	3138
	Ganymede	Galileo	1610	7.16	5262
	Callisto	Galileo	1610	16.69	4800
	Amalthea	Barnard	1892	0.50	200
	Himalia	Perrine	1904	251	180
	Elara	Perrine	1905	260	80
	Pasiphae	Melotte	1908	735	40
	Sinope	Nicholson	1914	738	40
	Lysithea	Nicholson	1938	259	40
	Carme	Nicholson	1938	692	40
	Ananke	Nicholson	1951	631	30
	Leda	Kowal	1974	239	15
	Thebe	Voyager	1979	0.67	90
	Adrastea	Voyager	1979	0.30	40
	Metis	Voyager	1979	0.29	20
	Callirrhoe	Scotti et al.	1999	—	—
	Themisto	Kowal & Roemer	1975	—	—
	Megaclite	Sheppard et al. #2	2000	—	—
	Taygete	Sheppard et al. #2	2000	—	—
	Chaldene	Sheppard et al. #2	2000	—	—
	Harpalyke	Sheppard et al. #2	2000	—	—
	Kalyke	Sheppard et al. #2	2000	—	—
	Iocaste	Sheppard et al. #2	2000	—	—
	Erinome	Sheppard et al. #2	2000	—	—

MOONS (cont.)

Planet	Satellite	Discoverer	Date	Period (days)	Size (km)
Jupiter	Isonoe	Sheppard et al. #2	2000	—	—
	Praxidike	Sheppard et al. #2	2000	—	—
	Autonoe	Sheppard et al. #3	2001	—	—
	Thyone	Sheppard et al. #3	2001	—	—
	Hermippe	Sheppard et al. #3	2001	—	—
	Aitne	Sheppard et al. #3	2001	—	—
	Eurydome	Sheppard et al. #3	2001	—	—
	Euanthe	Sheppard et al. #3	2001	—	—
	Euporie	Sheppard et al. #3	2001	—	—
	Orthosie	Sheppard et al. #3	2001	—	—
	Sponde	Sheppard et al. #3	2001	—	—
	Kale	Sheppard et al. #3	2001	—	—
	Pasithee	Sheppard et al. #3	2001	—	—
	Hegemone	Sheppard	2003	—	—
	Mneme	Gladman & Allen	2003	—	—
	Aoede	Sheppard	2003	—	—
	Thelxinoe	Sheppard	2003	—	—
	Arche	Sheppard	2002	—	—
	Kallichore	Sheppard	2003	—	—
	Helike	Sheppard	2003	—	—
	Carpo	Sheppard	2003	—	—
	Eukelade	Sheppard	2003	—	—
	Cyllene	Sheppard	2003	—	—
	Kore	Sheppard et al. #3	2003	—	—
Saturn	Mimas	Herschel	1789	0.94	394
	Enceladus	Herschel	1789	1.37	502
	Tethys	Cassini	1684	1.89	1048
	Dione	Cassini	1684	2.74	1120
	Rhea	Cassini	1672	4.52	1530

MOONS (cont.)

Planet	Satellite	Discoverer	Date	Period (days)	Size (km)
Saturn	Titan	Huygens	1655	15.95	5150
	Hyperion	Bond & Lassell	1848	21.3	270
	Iapetus	Cassini	1671	79.3	1435
	Phoebe	Pickering	1898	550	220
	Janus	Dolifus	1966	0.69	190
	Epimetheus	Fountain & Larson	1980	0.69	120
	Helene	Lecacheux & Laques	1980	2.74	30
	Telesto	Reitsema et al.	1980	1.89	25
	Calypso	Pascu et al.	1980	1.89	25
	Atlas	Voyager	1980	0.60	40
	Prometheus	Voyager	1980	0.61	80
	Pandora	Voyager	1980	0.63	100
	Pan	Showalter	1990	—	—
	Ymir	Gladman et al. #1	2000	—	—
	Paaliaq	Gladman et al. #1	2000	—	—
	Tarvos	Gladman et al. #1	2000	—	—
	Ijiraq	Gladman et al. #1	2000	—	—
	Suttungr	Gladman et al. #1	2000	—	—
	Kiviuq	Gladman et al. #1	2000	—	—
	Mundilfari	Gladman et al. #1	2000	—	—
	Albiorix	Holman	2000	—	—
	Skathi	Gladman et al. #1	2000	—	—
	Erriapus	Gladman et al. #1	2000	—	—
	Siarnaq	Gladman et al. #1	2000	—	—
	Thrymr	Gladman et al. #1	2000	—	—
	Narvi	Sheppard et al. #3	2003	—	—
	Methone	Cassini Team	2004	—	—
	Pallene	Cassini Team	2004	—	—
	Polydeuces	Cassini Team	2004	—	—
	Daphnis	Cassini Team	2005	—	—

Planet	Satellite	Discoverer	Date	Period (days)	Size (km)
Saturn	Aegir	Sheppard et al. #3	2004	—	—
	Bebhionn	Sheppard et al. #3	2004	—	—
	Bergelmir	Sheppard et al. #3	2004	—	—
	Bestla	Sheppard et al. #3	2004	—	—
	Farbauti	Sheppard et al. #3	2004	—	—
	Fenrir	Sheppard et al. #3	2004	—	—
	Fornjot	Sheppard et al. #3	2004	—	—
	Hati	Sheppard et al. #3	2004	—	—
	Hyrrokkin	Sheppard et al. #3	2004	—	—
	Kari	Sheppard et al. #3	2006	—	—
	Loge	Sheppard et al. #3	2006	—	—
	Skoll	Sheppard et al. #3	2006	—	—
	Surtur	Sheppard et al. #3	2006	—	—
	Anthe	Cassini Team	2007	—	—
	Jarnsaxa	Sheppard et al. #3	2006	—	—
	Greip	Sheppard et al. #3	2006	—	—
	Tarqeq	Sheppard et al. #3	2007	—	—
	Aegaeon	Cassini Team	2008	—	—
Uranus	Cordelia	Voyager	1986	0.34	40
	Ophelia	Voyager	1986	0.38	50
	Bianca	Voyager	1986	0.44	50
	Cressida	Voyager	1986	0.46	60
	Desdemona	Voyager	1986	0.48	60
	Juliet	Voyager	1986	0.50	80
	Portia	Voyager	1986	0.51	80
	Rosalind	Voyager	1986	0.56	60
	Belinda	Voyager	1986	0.63	60
	Puck	Voyager	1985	0.76	170
	Miranda	Kuiper	1948	1.41	200

Planet	Satellite	Discoverer	Date	Period (days)	Size (km)
Uranus	Ariel	Lassell	1851	2.52	1160
	Umbriel	Lassell	1851	4.14	1190
	Titania	Herschel	1787	8.71	1610
	Oberon	Herschel	1787	13.5	1550
	Caliban	Gladman et al. #2	1997	—	—
	Sycorax	Nicholson et al.	1997	—	—
	Prospero	Holman et al. #1	1999	—	—
	Setebos	Kavelaars et al. #1	1999	—	—
	Stephano	Gladman et al. #3	1999	—	—
	Trinculo	Holman et al. #2	2001	—	—
	Francisco	Kavelaars et al. #2	2001	—	—
	Margaret	Sheppard & Jewitt	2003	—	—
	Ferdinand	Milisavljevic et al.	2001	—	—
	Perdita	Karkoschka	1986	—	—
	Mab	Showalter & Lissauer	2003	—	—
	Cupid	Showalter & Lissauer	2003	—	—
Neptune	Naiad	Voyager	1989	0.30	50
	Thalassa	Voyager	1989	0.31	90
	Despina	Voyager	1989	0.33	150
	Galatea	Voyager	1989	0.40	150
	Larissa	Voyager	1989	0.55	200
	Proteus	Voyager	1989	1.12	400
	Triton	Lassell	1846	5.88	2720
	Nereid	Kuiper	1949	360	340
	Halimede	Holman et al. #3	2002	—	—
	Psamathe	Sheppard et al. #3	2003	—	—
	Sao	Grav et al.	2002	—	—
	Laomedeia	Kavelaars et al. #3	2002	—	—
	Neso	Holman et al. #3	2002	—	—

SOLAR ECLIPSES

Year	Date	Totality (minutes)	Locations
2010	July 11	5.3	South Pacific Ocean
2012	November 13	4.0	Northern Australia, South Pacific Ocean
2013	November 3	1.7	Atlantic Ocean, Central Africa
2015	March 20	4.1	North Atlantic Ocean, Arctic Ocean
2016	March 9	4.5	Indonesia, Pacific Ocean
2017	August 21	2.7	Pacific Ocean, USA, Atlantic Ocean
2019	July 2	4.5	South Pacific Ocean, South America
2020	December 14	2.2	South Pacific Ocean, South America
2021	December 4	1.9	Antarctica
2023	April 20	1.3	Indian Ocean, Indonesia
2024	April 8	4.5	South Pacific Ocean, Mexico, Eastern US
2026	August 12	2.3	Arctic, Greenland, North Atlantic, Spain
2027	August 2	6.4	North Africa, Arabia, Indian Ocean
2028	July 22	5.1	Indian Ocean, Australia, New Zealand
2030	November 25	3.7	South Africa, Indian Ocean, Australia

CONSTELLATIONS

Constellation	Genitive Case	English Name	Abbrev
Andromeda	Andromedae	Princess of Ethiopia	And
Antlia	Antliae	Air Pump	Ant
Apus	Apodis	Bird of Paradise	Aps
Aquaris	Aquarii	Water Bearer	Aqr
Aquila	Aquilae	Eagle	Aql
Ara	Arae	Altar	Ara
Aries	Arietis	Ram	Ari
Auriga	Aurigae	Charioteer	Aur
Bootes	Bootis	Herdsman	Boo
Caelum	Caeli	Graving Tool	Cae
Camelopardus	Camelopardis	Giraffe	Cam
Cancer	Cancri	Crab	Cnc
Canes Venatici	Canum Venaticorum	Hunting Dogs	CVn
Canis Major	Canis Majoris	Big Dog	CMa
Canis Minor	Canis Minoris	Little Dog	CMi
Capricornus	Capricorni	Sea Goat	Cap
Carina	Carinae	Keel of the Argonaut	Car
Cassiopeia	Cassiopeiae	Queen of Ethiopia	Cas
Centaurus	Centauri	Centaur	Cen
Cephus	Cephei	King of Ethiopia	Cep
Cetus	Ceti	Sea Monster (Whale)	Cet
Chamaeleon	Chamaeleontis	Chameleon	Cha
Circinus	Circini	Compasses	Cir
Columba	Columbae	Dove	Col
Coma Berenices	Comae Berenices	Berenice's hair	Com
Corona Australis	Coronae Australis	Southern Crown	CrA
Corona Borealis	Coronae Borealis	Northern Crown	CrB
Corvus	Corvi	Crow	Crv
Crater	Crateris	Cup	Crt
Crux	Crucis	Southern Cross	Cru
Cygnus	Cygni	Swan	Cyg

CONSTELLATIONS (cont.)

Constellation	Genitive Case	English Name	Abbrev
Delphinus	Delphini	Dolphin	Del
Dorado	Doradus	Swordfish	Dor
Draco	Draconis	Dragon	Dra
Equuleus	Equulei	Little Horse	Equ
Eridanus	Eridani	River	Eri
Fornax	Fornacis	Furnace	For
Gemini	Geminorum	Twins	Gem
Grus	Gruis	Crane	Gru
Hercules	Herculis	Hercules	Her
Horologium	Horologii	Clock	Hor
Hydra	Hydrae	Sea Serpent	Hya
Hydrus	Hydri	Water Snake	Hyi
Indus	Indi	Indian	Ind
Lacerta	Lacertae	Lizard	Lac
Leo	Leonis	Lion	Leo
Leo Minor	Leonis Minoris	Little Lion	LMi
Lepus	Leporis	Hare or Rabbit	Lep
Libra	Librae	Balance	Lib
Lupus	Lupi	Wolf	Lup
Lynx	Lyncis	Lynx	Lyn
Lyra	Lyrae	Lyre or Harp	Lyr
Mensa	Mensae	Table Mountain	Men
Microscopium	Microscopii	Microscope	Mic
Monoceros	Monocerotis	Unicorn	Mon
Musca	Muscae	Fly	Mus
Norma	Normae	Carpenter's Level	Nor
Octans	Octantis	Octant	Oct
Ophiuchus	Ophiuchi	Holder of Serpent	Oph
Orion	Orionis	Orion the Hunter	Ori
Pavo	Pavonis	Peacock	Pav
Pegasus	Pegasi	Pegaus, Winged Horse	Peg

CONSTELLATIONS (cont.)

Constellation	Genitive Case	English Name	Abbrev
Perseus	Persei	Perseus the Hero	Per
Phoenix	Phoenicis	Phoenix	Phe
Pictor	Pictoris	Easel	Pic
Pisces	Piscium	Fishes	Psc
Piscis Austrinus	Piscis Austrini	Southern Fish	PsA
Puppis	Puppis	Stern of the Argonaut	Pup
Pyxis	Pyxidus	Compass of the Argonaut	Pyx
Reticulum	Reticuli	Net	Ret
Sagitta	Sagittae	Arrow	Sge
Sagittarius	Sagittarii	Archer	Sgr
Scorpius	Scorpii	Scorpion	Sco
Sculptor	Sculptoris	Sculptor's Tools	Scl
Scutum	Scuti	Shield	Sct
Serpens	Serpentis	Serpent	Ser
Sextans	Sexantis	Sextant	Sex
Taurus	Tauri	Bull	Tau
Telescopium	Telescopii	Telescope	Tel
Triangulum	Trianguli	Triangle	Tri
Triangulum Australe	Trainguli Australis	Southern Triangle	TrA
Tucana	Tucanae	Toucan	Tuc
Ursa Major	Ursae Majoris	Big Bear	UMa
Ursa Minor	Ursae Minoris	Little Bear	UMi
Vela	Velorum	Sail of Argonauts' Ship	Vel
Virgo	Virginis	Virgin	Vir
Volans	Volantis	Flying Fish	Vol
Vulpecula	Vulpeculae	Fox	Vul

BRIGHTEST STARS

Star	Constellation	Season	Mag	Color	Distance
Sirius	Canis Major	Winter	−1.5	White	9
Canopus	Carina	Winter*	−0.7	White	100
Alpha Centaurus	Centaurus	Spring*	−0.1	Yellow	4
Arcturus	Bootes	Spring	−0.1	Orange	36
Vega	Lyra	Summer	+0.0	White	25
Capella	Auriga	Winter	+0.1	Yellow	45
Rigel	Orion	Winter	+0.1	Blue	815
Procyon	Canis Minor	Winter	+0.4	Yellow	11
Betelgeuse	Orion	Winter	+0.4	Orange	490
Achernar	Eridanus	Autumn*	+0.5	Blue	65
Beta Centaurus	Centaurus	Spring*	+0.6	Blue	290
Altair	Aquila	Summer	+0.8	White	17
Alpha Crucis	Southern Cross	Spring*	+0.9	Blue	390
Aldebaran	Taurus	Winter	+0.9	Orange	50
Spica	Virgo	Spring	+0.9	Blue	260
Antares	Scorpius	Summer	+0.9	Orange	390
Pollux	Gemini	Winter	+1.1	Yellow	40
Fomalhaut	Pisces Austrinus	Autumn*	+1.2	White	23
Deneb	Cygnus	Summer	+1.3	White	1400
Beta Crucis	Southern Cross	Spring*	+1.3	Blue	490

*Visible in the Southern Hemisphere during the indicated Northern Hemisphere season.

The distances are in light years.

REFERENCES

Books

Star Names: Their Lore and Meaning
Richard Hinckley Allen
(Dover Publications: New York, NY), 1963
[ISBN 0-486-21079-0]

Burnham's Celestial Handbook: An Observer's Guide to the Universe Beyond the Solar System
Robert Burnham, Jr.
(Dover Publications: New York, NY), 1978
[ISBN 0-486-24063-0]

The Stars: A New Way to See Them
H.A. Rey
(Houghton Mifflin Company: Boston, MA), 1980
[ISBN 978-0547132808]

The New Patterns in the Sky, (Myths and Legends of the Stars)
Julius D.W. Staal
(McDonald & Woodward Publishing Company: Blacksburg, VA), 1988
[ISBN 978-0939923045]

Magazines

Astronomy Magazine
Kalmbach Publishing
21027 Crossroads Circle
Waukesha, WI 53187-1612
(800) 533-6644
www.astronomy.com

Sky & Telescope Magazine
Sky Publishing
90 Sherman Street
Cambridge, MA 02140
(800) 253-0245
www.skyandtelescope.com

Organizations

American Astronomical Society (AAS)
2000 Florida Avenue, Suite 400
Washington, DC 20009-1231
(202) 328-2010
www.aas.org

Astronomical Society of the Pacific (ASP)
390 Ashton Avenue
San Francisco, CA 94112
(415) 337-1100
www.astrosociety.org

American Association of Variable Star Observers (AAVSO)
49 Bay State Road
Cambridge, MA 02138-1205
(617) 354-0484
www.aavso.org

Association of Lunar and Planetary Observers (ALPO)
PO Box 13456
Springfield, IL 62791-3456
www.alpo-astronomy.org

International Dark-Sky Association (IDA)
3225 N. First Avenue
Tucson, AZ 85719
(520) 327-9331
www.darksky.org